To David —
From
Pat.
Sept. 19th 1983.

Prelude to BATTLE

Prelude to BATTLE

Gordon Moore

MIDAS BOOKS
Tunbridge Wells

HIPPOCRENE BOOKS INC
New York

In the same military experiences series:
So they Rode & Fought by Major General S. S. Hamid
Stoker Greenwood's Navy by Sydney Greenwood
For You the War is Over by Philip Kindersley
The Yanks are Coming by John Frayn Turner & Eddie Hale
Prelude to Battle by Gordon Moore
The Bader Wing by John Frayn Turner *
Eighth Army Driver by Maurice Merritt

First published UK in 1983 by
MIDAS BOOKS
12 Dene Way, Speldhurst,
Tunbridge Wells, Kent TN3 0NX.

© Gordon Moore 1983

ISBN 0 85936 119 5 (UK)

First published USA in 1983 by
HIPPOCRENE BOOKS INC
171 Madison Avenue,
New York, NY 10016.

ISBN 0 88254 745 3 (USA)

Phototypesetting by Studio .918, Tunbridge Wells, Kent.
Printed and bound in Great Britain by Camelot Press, Southampton.

PRELUDE TO BATTLE

This is the story of a young infantry soldier in World War Two; the story of life in England during the build up for the invasion of Europe, in 1944.

It is an account of the training and social life of a group of eighteen year old boys, who, two years later, were to be deposited in Normandy, to take their place in the spearhead of the British/Canadian offensive, as the pivot of the Allied thrust.

There is a lot of humour, because, in spite of the realism of training, and the news from the Middle East and Far East fronts, there can be no comparison between this life and the reality, which was the mainland of Europe, in 1944.

After basic infantry training, we follow the author through specialist training, for infantry support groups. Certain regiments – there were four of them – consisted of troops, trained especially to man the Vickers machine gun and the dreaded 4.2-inch mortar; so one of these regiments featured in every division.

In spite of the rigours of preparing for this most epic invasion in history, life was often exciting and enjoyable, with the bonuses of comradeship, and the opportunity to stretch fledgling wings, away from the parental nest. Most of the young men had had little experience of travel. Holidays away from home were not common in the thirties, and the girls from far away towns and villages were there to be wooed, and perhaps won. Social education, in schools or youth clubs, was scanty, or non-existent.

Yes, they were great days. But on the horizon there was something else – all this was a prelude – everybody was aware of it, but few gave it too much consideration. Many would not get through unscathed, but each one rated his own chances high. There were, too, the agonising times of waiting and wondering, for parents, brothers and sisters, back home.

The stiffening of older, battle-tested soldiers to be found in the combat battalions, shrugged their shoulders. 'If your number was up, you would get it – it would get you.' It was this fatalistic attitude that carried many of them through the times ahead.

The story is mostly fact, with incidents amalgamated and modified, to give greater coherence and interest. The places are real, and many of the people are real – others, again, are amalgams of several met during the years 1942-1944.

The account of the training is pretty accurate, but a few of the 'social' incidents have been modified, in order to portray the essential atmosphere of the times. All names of characters have been changed, with one notable exception.

I hope that younger readers might come to appreciate the tremendous upheaval which occurred in the lives of fathers and uncles – and, indeed, grandfathers! Perhaps the older readers will give a few wry smiles, and, through the story, remember some of their own experiences of the times.

ABBREVIATIONS

ATS	Auxillary Territorial Service
BD	Battle Dress
CO	Commanding Officer
CSM	Company Sergeant Major
FFI	Free From Infection
FMO	Full Marching Order
FSMO	Field Service Marching Order
GI	American Soldier
LMG	Light Machine Gun
M and D	Medicine and Duty
MMG	Medium Machine Gun
MI	Medical Inspection
MO	Medical Officer
MGTC	Machine Gun Training Centre
MP	Military Police
NAAFI	Navy, Army and Air Force Institutes
NCO	Non-commissioned Officer
OR	Other Rank
PT	Physical Training
PTW	Primary Training Wing
PU	Pick Up
QAIMNS	Queen Alexandra's Imperial Military Nursing Service
RAOC	Royal Army Ordnance Corps
RASC	Royal Army Service Corps
RA	Royal Artillery
REME	Royal Electrical and Mechanical Engineers
RE	Royal Engineers
RNF	Royal Northumberland Fusiliers
RP	Regimental Policeman
RQMS	Regimental Quartermaster Sergeant
RSM	Regimental Sergeant-Major
RTO	Railway Transport Officer
SMLE	Short Muzzle Lee Enfield
TCV	Troop Carrying Vehicle
WAAF	Women's Auxiliary Air Force
WO	Warrant Officer
VAD	Voluntary Aid Detachment

Chapter One

'Left, Right, Left, Right; Left . . . . . Left! Pick those feet up! Don't bend yer elbows! Squaaad, Halt! Squaaad, Di-i-is-mis! Don't ferget ter salute the officer. Up, two three, left, two, three. . .'

The denim-clad platoon clattered off to the NAAFI. In fifteen minutes time, they would assemble in the drill shed, to be shown the mechanics of the SMLE rifle.

I hurried with the rest of the mob to get into the queue. The line moved quickly, as the girls behind the counter dispensed the thick cups, slopping with dark fluid – NAAFI tea! Somebody rattled the piano. Someone started to croak the words of the current hit, *I got Bells that Jingle, Jangle, Jingle.*

The wind whistled across the open ground, straight from the distant peaks of North Wales, and into the open drill shed.

'This, 'ere is the pull through, and this is a piece of four by two. . .'

I moved from one foot to the other. ''ere we 'ave the fore sight, and this 'ere, is the back sight. Get the tip of the fore sight in the centre of the U. . .' My mind started to wander – to effect an escape from the grinding tedium of the endless hours of instruction and discomfort. However, all good things come to an end, and I was jerked back to the grim present.

'C'pral 'Olmes, double these men away.'

'Right, Sar'nt.'

'I'll meet you, out on the field, in five minutes – Move!'

'Yes, Sar'nt. Move in to line, you lot. Move! Squaaad, Squaaad, 'Shun! Left turn. By the left, Double March! Left, Right, Left. . .'

We doubled, smartly, to the training field, at the edge of the camp, rifles at the trail. Sergeant Jacks saw us coming. He took a last, long pull at his fag, and trod the stub into the coarse turf. Unlike the others, he was dressed in battle dress serge, with well-blancoed anklets web, over his dubbinned boots. 'Six weeks to get this shower in to some sort of order, and then another lot!' He was in his middle thirties; short, with a red, angry complexion, and the top missing from his left, index finger. An East Londoner, he had joined the regiment in 1930. He had seen some action in North India, packing the machine gun on stubborn mules, and firing long bursts of .303 across the sun-baked valleys at elusive tribesmen. This was different, but a bloody sight safer! His two NCOs, Corporal Foot and Lance-Corporal Holmes, were good, reliable men. Foot was a regular, from his own regiment, and Holmes came from Manchester, where he had left the dance band and the Westminster

Bank, and joined up with the Manchesters. He was not a regular, and was younger – not a lot older than the rookies in No 2 Platoon, 'A' Company, Primary Wing, attached to 24 Machine Gun Training Centre.

Corporal Holmes halted us, in true military fashion, we dressed from the right, and handed over to the sergeant.

'Thank you, Corpral Holmes. Number 1 Section – C'pral Foot, 'ere's your shower. C'pral 'Olmes, you take No. 2 – an' No 3, you come with me.'

I trailed along, with the rest of No. 3 section, to where the sergeant was waiting. We were on a piece of waste ground, behind the square. The sparse, sour grass, was interspersed with puddles, and the whole area had been well churned up by countless hundreds of army boots, stamping, dragging or scrabbling over it. The cold, damp, autumn wind blew across from the hills. Nearby, members of No 1 platoon were being, similarly instructed.

This was it! Four days in the Army – vaccinated, injected, tested, kitted out, drilled – and now – a real rifle! True, it was an old one, but it was still a real one. This thing shot death-dealing bullets. It wasn't an air gun.

'Line up, along 'ere. Wot's your name, son?' Sergeant Jacks thrust his red, pugnacious face forward, and scowled at me.

'George Milton.'

'George Milton, what?'

'George Milton, Sergeant,' I added, hastily.

'Wot's your number?'

'14162034, Sergeant.'

'14162034, Private Milton, G., and don't you ferget it!' was the sharp reminder.

'No, Sergeant,' I promised, anxious to divert the focus of attention to some other poor section member.

'Wot's it say, on them bloody tags around yore neck, aye? Don't you bleedin' ferget it.'

'No Sergeant.'

Blimey! Already there were a lot of things you don't forget – your rifle is your best friend; you salute all officers, of all Allied nations and both sexes; you don't salute the RSM, on pain of death! You don't walk across the square, if you know what's good for you; you don't turn up, late, for anything. You volunteered to join this sort of mob, but you don't volunteer for anything else, now you're here.

'Right, now 'old yor rifle like this, in yer left 'and, sling loose. Not like that – 'old it at the point of balance. As y'were.' We were off again, and it paid to take notice. Sergeant Jacks had a knack of asking awkward questions of the very bloke who wasn't paying attention. 'Now these rounds of .303 ammunition are dummies.

I've got a lot of bleedin' dummies ararnd 'ere, today! All these
dummies are painted red. Collard, you ought ter be painted bloody
red! If it ain't red, then don't play with it, 'ere, or you'll blow
somebody's bloody 'ead orf. When you load 'em in the clip, do it
like this. If you do it wrong, they'll get stuck in the magazine, and a
bloody great Jerry'll 'ave 'is bayonet in your stones, before you can
get 'im. When yer get down, yer do it fast – like this.' For all his age
and blanco, the sergeant suddenly fell flat on the ground. He
seemed to hover in the air, for a second, and then he was down; he
fell horizontally, for a second, and he was lying with his whole body
hugging the ground. His head was buried in the grass. He got up.
'Ready, you lot. Down! Spread yer legs, an' keep yer 'ead down.
Get up! Down! Up!' He looked pained, and turned, with an
expression of resignation or distaste, to Lance Corporal Holmes.
'Lance C'pral 'Olmes.'

'Yes, Sergeant.'

'This lot'll 'ave to 'ave some practice after tea – they're idle! See
to it, Corporal.'

'Yes, Sergeant.'

He hadn't finished with us, yet. 'Again! Down! Keep yer 'ead
down – never mind the puddles. Up! Down! Up! What's yor name,
son?'

This time, it was somebody else's turn to receive the Sergeant's
undivided attention.

'14162046, Collard, G., Sergeant.'

'Well, 046 Private Collard, you've got ter smarten up. Look at
yer belt. Yer pack should be resting up there, not down on yer arse!'
He shoved Collard's pack up, vigorously, and shortened some of
the straps. 'Lance C'pral 'Olmes!'

'Coming, Sergeant.'

'See this man smartens up. A German might die of larfin' if 'e
sees 'im.' Poor Geoff Collard was already No 2 platoon odd man
out. An intelligent lad, from Canterbury, he was the butt of the
NCOs. His equipment never seemed to sit properly on his lanky
frame; his arms and legs often failed to synchronise when he
marched on the square; his very background of good grammar
school, classical music, his preference for a cup of coffee in the
Kardomah, his awkwardness in all things physical – all these
characteristics made him stick out like a sore thumb. Most of the
recruits were from the London area – survivors – wise, instead of
merely clever; tough and gregarious; impervious to most of the
vagaries of the system.

I was another grammar school boy who had volunteered. I too
stuck out a bit from most of the intake, but my background had
been a harder one. I had had to learn to be a survivor at home, and I
was already finding some kindred spirits among the Cockney

11

element. My village home was near Slough, and I had worked for two years before joining up. Even so, I was green – very green – and I had to take a bit of leg pulling from the city boys.

The afternoon wore on, and we loaded, fired our dummies, unloaded, collected the dummy rounds from the mud, re-set our sights, and started all over again. I lay, prone, and clicked my rifle. I cuddled it and got used to drawing it firmly into my shoulder. We had already been fed some nasty stories of broken shoulders caused by the recoil of a rifle. Click. Ease the bolt. Click! God! Two weeks ago I was with my mates, in the lab. at work. What were they doing? They'd have had the afternoon cup of tea, brought round on the trolly by poor old Ivy. They'd be thinking of knocking off time – scrubbing up in the wash rooms; trying to remove the multi-colours of the pigments and resins that they had been working with. Later, they would be going to a dance, or to the inevitable evening class associated with the type of work that they were on.

The Welsh Hills were beginning to fade; the air was getting chilly.

'Well, you lot; you are a bloody shower. You'll 'ave ter learn ter move, Army style. You'll 'ave ter be a bit more jilty. Straighten up – you're in a worse state than bloody Russia. C'pral Foot, get this lot fell in, and take 'EM AWAY.'

'Thank Christ for that!' muttered someone. At least the agony was over for a while. We could get back to the barrack room, get cleaned up and down for tea – probably pilchards.

We got our 'irons', and we were marched off. After tea, we could get our beds down, and, perhaps, spend an hour or two in town. What with 'jabs', and interviews with the platoon commander, Lieutenant Childs – fairly new from OCTU – there had been no time up to now; a couple of hours in the NAAFI had been about it.

The Machine Gun Training Centre was a large barracks, consisting of permanent buildings, and surrounded by wooden huts. The barrack block housed the Primary Training Wing, and the regimental lines of the four county regiments were in the wooden hut, in their own corners of the camp. It was about a mile to Chester and on the main Liverpool Road. After six weeks in primary training, recruits were assigned to their regiment that they had signed for when volunteering, providing they came up to scratch. Operating the machine gun called for fitness and a certain kind of nimbleness. If you didn't make it, you went to some other unit.

There was just time for a shower. I changed into second best battle dress, ready to go out after tea. Our section was marched down to the cookhouse. It was pilchards, as I had thought. After tea we washed our 'irons' in the tub of hot water by the door.

'Coming down town, George?' The speaker was Bill Smith.

'Yeah,' I replied, 'We could have a pint or two.'

'Why, you got some dosh left, then?' Bill looked up with his sharp, shrewd eyes. He was from Peckham, and used to work in a wireless repair shop. 'I'm skint till Thursday.'

'I got a few bob left,' I assured him; 'I'll get one in.'

'We might find a bit of grumble at the arcade. They 'ang ararnd there. That's right, ain't it, Jim?' He turned to Jim for assurance that the amusement arcade was a Mecca for lonely recruits.

'Yeah,' replied Jim, ' 'ang ararnd, waiting for it.'

It had taken a bit of time for the out-of-town boys to get used to the vernacular. I was rapidly catching up on a new language.

Boots clean, buttons polished, those who hoped to go out for an hour or two marched briskly in twos and threes towards the main gate. I was with Bill Smith and another lad from our platoon, and we filed into the guard room to sign out. The sergeant in charge of the guard scrutinised us, Christ! Surely, he wasn't going to find something wrong.

'Do your neck up, soldier.' He spoke curtly, and Jim, my other mate, hastily complied.

'Yes, Sergeant,' he replied, doing up the offending button.

'And you'd better get them trousers under the bed, tonight. You got more lines there than Clapham Junction. Go on. You get by, this time, but you'll 'ave to sharpen up a bit, or the ladies are going to miss some of your wit and charm.'

'Thank you, Sergeant,' said Jim, gratefully. They signed out, thankful to have passed muster. We walked into the city, along the main road, coming in through the city wall, in to the main street. This was a garrison town, well immured to the presence of soldiery. Through the distant centuries, this had been a border town, built and manned to keep out the pestilent Welsh tribes. We cluttered along the pavement, keeping a wary eye open for officers and MPs. The town was full of servicemen of all arms. There was a fair sprinkling of GIs from the US Army division deployed around the district.

'Let's go in *The Crown*,' said Bill. We trooped in, and I bought three halves, seeing that the other two hung back a bit. We found space on a bench by the wall, and sat down. The bar was crowded. Three ATS came in and looked cooly in our direction, obviously not very impressed with what they saw. They knew their market value, and raw recruits weren't really in the bidding. A couple of local girls sat, giggling, on the next bench. Again, with very little money, we were on a loser. These girls were quickly chatted up by two slick corporals from the RNFs, who were also stationed at the MGTC.

'Who wants a snout?' asked Bill, with a sigh.

'Ta, Bill,' said Jim, taking one from the proffered crumpled packet.

He shoved the packet at me. 'George?'

'No, thanks, Bill,' I said. I watched them cadge a light from the end of a fag at the next table. The pair of them sat there, tapping the ash nervously and looking around at the 'talent' in the bar, inhaling deeply. I had never smoked. There was no way I would have dared, at home. My father was an inveterate smoker who had practically furnished the home on coupons obtained from Ardath cigarettes. Like many others of his time, he was violently opposed to his sons becoming the addict that he had become. Anyway, what with my working in a paint lab, and the athletics training, there had been no room for such vices, or any others worth having for that matter. I was still in touch with the old club, where I had been the local 'star' middle distance man. In fact, my social life had been far from exciting – the people I met being largely restricted to those I met at evening classes and a few mates at work – and most of them I had known at school. My local grammar school had been a 'boys only'. True, I had a brother, but not a sister. Up to now, life had been pretty sheltered, and any problems that might arise with an adolescent boy were strictly taboo. Dad was strict, arbitrary and not very approachable for much of the time, and Mum was out of her depth. The biology lessons had been some help, and the rest came from the usual conversations with the boys. Chatting up girls had not featured in any curriculum.

'There's no bloody talent here,' said Bill. 'Let's go somewhere else.'

We drained our half pint glasses, and threaded our way through the crowded bar. Outside, a sailor was squatting on his haunches on the edge of the pavement, being mildly sick in the gutter. A group of four boisterous WAAFs came along the pavement, sweeping all before them. We cluttered awkwardly down the street, trying to appear as if we were part of the surging tide of military manhood. We circumnavigated groups of servicemen, and looked around for a quiet pub. Down by the river, just out of the centre of town, we came across *The Jolly Boatman*. It was crowded. Parties of drinkers were still spilling out of the bar, along the river bank. A trooper in the RA unit at the castle was spread out by a scrubby hawthorne bush, in passionate confrontation with a girl. She was trying desperately, and almost successfully, to keep his wandering hands and hungry lips within the bounds of decency. I had managed to fight my way to the bar where a sweating, hard-pressed barman had pulled me three halves. I forced my way outside, precariously balancing the third glass between the other two.

'Had to find some empty glasses before he'd serve me,' I explained.

'Cor, look at 'im,' said Jim Dodson. 'Bloody 'ell, he'll be 'avin' 'er drawers down in a minute!'

Like the other new boys, Jim was only eighteen. But he had worked on his father's farm near Staines, and he had seen something of the occasional man-hungry land-girl, out among the stooks of corn when the lunch time cider and baking sun sometimes made a lonely afternoon infinitely exciting. The amorous trooper had got as far as local circumstances would permit, and he was earnestly trying to persuade the girl to move to a more secluded place. Although she tried, belatedly, to play 'hard to get', it was fairly obvious to the more experienced observers that he was going to make it. The sky had darkened into night and a cool autumn breeze had sprung up, making little cats-paws at the water's edge. With mock chidings of 'do be'ave yourself, Fred,' the girl allowed herself to be led away.

Bill gave a sigh. 'Not much talent around 'ere, and what there is, is all booked up.'

I gave a wise grunt of agreement. Me, who had hardly ever spoken to a girl, except in the course of work. True, I once took my partner from dancing classes to a dance in Slough. It had been a sort of continuation of the class. It had been quite a palaver, going to call for her and meeting her Mum. I had taken her home at the end, in a dutiful manner, and I hadn't even kissed her Goodnight. I got on OK with the lads, and I could mix with the next one, but my desperate fear of the young ladies had not been eased by home environment. I had never kissed a girl, but I had dreamed of putting my hand in a girl's blouse, or up her skirt, like the trooper had done. It was a depressing business, and I felt rather sad and inadequate.

'Abart time we got a shift on,' said Bill. 'I got ter put me bed down.'

'Didn't you do that before we came out?' I asked, jolted back to the present by his Cockney voice.

'No, I was blancoing me belt, in the drying room,' he explained.

'Come on, then,' said Jim. We stood up. Bill stamped his feet to shake his trouser bottoms into place over his boots. We walked along briskly, through the edge of the town back towards camp.

The ring of our studded boots on the metalled road was a solid reminder that we were soldiers, and, already, I had a feeling that we were something alien, apart from the natives of the Cheshire countryside.

'Watch it,' murmured Bill, 'there's a couple of red caps over there.' Sure enough, two corporals of the Military Police were walking, in step and with measured tread, towards the centre of the town. Their red-topped caps could just be made out in the dim light of the blacked-out street. However, the policemen weren't bothered about a bunch of harmless rookies. Their business was in the centre of town, where fights were likely to break out as the pubs shut. The town was the assembly point of a vast concourse of military and civilians – British, Canadian, Polish, American – all were there, and friction there often was. British soldiers, jealous of the GIs superior spending power and access to nylon stockings and cigarettes, would sometimes erupt into frustrated violence. The girls had never had it so good. The Yanks were courteous and different. They knew how to charm a lady. Besides, there was always the chance of being taken back to the USA – land of promise – as a GI bride. The infantry boys would sometimes try to prove a point of virility after a few drinks, when regimental pride and 'honour' rose on a crest of mild and bitter. Regimental pride ran very high with the infantry. Apart from the Navy, Army and Air Force police, male and female, there were the civilian police and the dreaded American 'Snowdrops'. At the first hint of trouble involving GIs, they would arrive in battle wagons and clear the scene, with a liberal use of long batons, humping stunned rowdies aboard, and driving off. All in all though, in spite of the tensions, there was surprisingly little trouble. The military could make it pretty hard for their wrong doers, but the locals would allow the soldiers a fair leeway – it was pretty obvious that there would be some rough times ahead for some of them, and they weren't all going to make it. And, again, many of the locals had sons or daughters or husbands in similar situations somewhere else.

The next morning dawned like any other. At 6.30 the platoon members turned out in vests, shorts and boots. After a mug of hot tea, they went for their usual run. Then they went straight back to the barrack room washed, shaved, changed into denims, and paraded for breakfast, at 7.30. Before going to breakfast, blankets were folded in the approved fashion, and the bunk set out for inspection. After breakfast, the various sections took over areas of the parade ground for marching drill. Our platoon was in the charge of Corporal Foot. I stood easy, in the front rank, looking around. The corporal was a reasonable bloke, I thought, as long as he wasn't pushed too far.

'Squaaad –' As we stiffened, our right hands slid down the rifles. 'Squaaad – 'Shun! As y'were! Together, this time. Squaad – Squaaad, Shun! Slo – op arms! Platoon will move to the right in column of threes – Ri–ght turn! By the left, Quick march!'

The platoon was certainly sharpening up. Even Geoff Collard was keeping in step, and swinging his right arm in time with the rest.

'Pull on yer rifle, that man in the rear rank! Don't bend yer elbow, Private Collard! Left, right, left, right. . .' They manoeuvred up and down and across the tarmac square. Boots crunched in unison, right arms moved forward and backwards, as though pulled along by a string; the sloping rifles stayed firmly rooted on the left shoulders.

The barracks lined two sides of the square. The third side was lined by drill sheds, and the fourth side was open. Beyond it lay a vast area of waste ground, used for battle drill. In the distance lay the hills of Wales. The hour's drill over, our platoon was joined by Sergeant Jacks and Lance Corporal Holmes. Sergeant Jacks glared down the line.

'Collard, get that cap on straight – get yer button over yer right eye. Smith, get yours on right – you look like a tart on an Easter Parade. Lance Corporal 'Olmes, march the platoon over to the weapon training block.'

Holmes took over. The weapon training hut was a wooden classroom, with benches and trestle tables. Round the walls were charts of grenades, of several kinds. The thirty members of the platoon sat, squashed up, on the benches. At the front, behind a table, was Sergeant Wilson, the training sergeant of No 1 Platoon and an instructor in grenades. He had a grenade on the table, a box of others alongside. There followed an hour of instruction on the 36 Mills hand grenade, and dummy grenades were distributed among us. Horrific stories were related, about detonators that blew off fingers, of grenades that dropped back, after striking the parapet of a trench; of grenades that didn't explode. Instruction over we were split into three sections, to practise throwing dummy grenades over a piece of high wire netting. Our section was in the charge of Corporal Foot, who himself had a good arm.

'Right, I'll give a shilling to anyone who can lob one further than I can,' he challenged.

In turn, we lobbed our dummies over the wire. 'Chuck it up in the air. That gives it time for the fuse to burn, and it's more likely to explode – 'specially if the ground's soft. You don't want some cheeky bugger throwing it back at yer. . .'

My turn came. I was a tall, bony lad, and I had just spent the summer in athletics, and playing cricket for the Works' team. I had done some pretty keen practices to get in that cricket team, and I was a good fielder. Also, I had been watching points while the others were throwing. I picked up one of the dummies. I got a good grip on it, swung my arm well back, and hurled it, as though it had been some medieval device for throwing rocks over castle walls. It sailed over the wire, and landed, well beyond any previous mark. I felt a bit embarrased.

'Cor, 'ow abart that, Corp! That's a bob you owe 'im!'

The London boys of the section were pleased. To them, I was a bloke from the 'sticks', but I had got one up on the corporal, and they were pleased – and impressed.

'Alright, alright. We'll see.' Foot, a large man, hadn't expected to lose to one of us new lot, and he was a bit rattled.

'Come on, Corp; you 'ad a bet; payup!'

'Alright, shut up, you shower.' The good corporal was wriggling a bit, and covering up by 'pulling rank'. 'Remind me termorrer. Now, five minutes smoke. Them as 'asn't got any fags, can go through the motions.'

The section fell out. Some of the boys lit up – mostly tab ends, shaken out from a packet. Fags were hard to come by. The NAAFI quota of forty a week didn't go far. Of course, it helped having one or two non-smokers in the squad.

'Now, next week you're going ter throw a real one.' We all listened, duly impressed, while Foot went on. 'For Christ's sake keep a bloody grip on it, when you pull out the pin – just like Sar'nt Wilson showed yer. I don't particularly want to share one with you lot.' He took a draw on his fag, and we carried on talking, in little clusters.

During the afternoon, there was a lesson on the bren gun. This light machine gun (LMG), was the mainstay of the infantry platoon. There was one of them to each section, and all the men carried spare bren magazines in their pouches. Sergeant Jacks was at his most eloquent. Having explained the principles, he called for some action.

'Private Milton – you are number one. Get down behind that gun. Get down wiv 'im, Private Smith. You are number two.' We got down on the ground, as we had been shown. I pulled the butt up to my shoulder and curled my right index finger round the trigger. There wasn't a lot of time to dream, as the sergeant's staccato instructions cracked on my ears.

'Change magazine! Range 800, short bursts – Fire! Right o. Cease firing! Now, close that ejection opening cover, number one.'

I felt under the gun for the elusive slide. It was a job that had to be done by feel, as you couldn't see underneath. It was hard to find.

'Come on, private. . . Can't you find it? I shall 'ave ter put some 'air rahnd it for yer.' This was always good for a belly laugh, and the platoon duly obliged. I felt myself going a bit red, but I managed to find the cover, and I closed the damn thing, grateful.

'Fall out! Next two, down!' The pressure was off me, for a while, and I could dream away in the crowd.

The days wore on. There wasn't much time to fret.

'I gotta do in six weeks what took the bloody Army six months in peace time,' rasped Jacks. 'I gotta make soldiers of you lot – it gives me nightmares. As fer you, Collard – I ain't even sure who's side you're on.'

Most of the evenings were soaked up with lectures, tests, interviews, cleaning kit, or, in some cases, extra drills. There wasn't much time to go into town. There was always the NAAFI. You could get tea and a wad, or even a pint of luke warm beer, although it wasn't exactly the cosy atmosphere of the local pub. Inevitably, someone would strum the upright, untuned piano, and the soldiers would sit around at the tables. If you could get on the right side of a NAAFI girl, you might scrounge an extra packet of fags. The girls were oblivious to most blandishments. They had to survive among this rough, tough welter of soldiery, and they learned to cope. True, one occasionally left under mysterious circumstances, but mostly they survived. The one canteen served the whole camp, corporals and other ranks. The sergeants and warrant officers had their own mess. Most of the customers were in denims; rough, ill-fitting, battle-dress type overalls. Often tattered from much wear and laundering, they were usually worn for training and fatigues – that means most of the time. You collected a change of denims once a week, and you took what came.

On one such night, I was sitting with one or two of number two platoon at a slop-covered table, listening to the row on the piano. *I Got Bells that Jingle, Jangle, Jingle* was followed by *Tangerine*. These two songs were the rage, and could be heard, rendered in various dialects, and sometimes with amendments to the words, sung in snatches in barrack rooms and ablutions. The room was pretty full. As well as the new boys – still on primary training and wearing the general service badge in their forage caps – there were the Geordie boys, excitable, and usually keen to defend regimental and territorial honour; there were the more phlegmatic lads from Manchester and Cheshire, and there were the worldly wise boys from the Middlesex. Most of these regimental soldiers had recently completed their six weeks primary training, and were in various regimental lines, learning to handle the medium machine gun, as well as continuing with general infantry training. Added to these trainees, who would soon pass through the camp on postings, there were the general duties, headquarters and specialist staff who ran the centre – cooks, clerks, drivers, junior instructors, storemen, and low category infantry on general duties.

'Where do you come from, George?' John Lewin took a bite of bun and a gulp of tea. Like me, he didn't smoke and had been to grammar school, in Surrey somewhere. He had joined up for his own reasons as I had, and had chosen a combat arm of the Army. Most of our school mates had joined the RAF, and were training as air crew.

'Oh, a little place, near Slough,' I replied. Most of them had heard of Slough, but few of them would have heard of Iver. In one corner, a party of Geordies were waxing lyrical. Red faced and watery eyed, ringing a table, littered with half pint glasses, they were singing *Bladen Races,* in direct competition with the piano.

Bill Smith had been for a 'jimmy', and was walking back to join us, but he bumped their table in passing.

'Watch where yeer going, yer Cockney git!' slurred an offended Geordie, standing up, with a struggle, and squaring up to Bill. He was dragged back down by two mates.

'Aw, gang awa, Geordie, he's na warth the bother.'

'He ain't very friendly,' said the aggrieved Bill, as he rejoined our party.

'Nar, mate, they don't like Cockneys, especially when they get pissed! Give that one a smell of the bar-maid's apron, an' 'e's well away.' The speaker was a Londoner himself, from the Middlesex, and he was sitting quietly with a mate.

It was nearly time to go back to the barrack room. The NAAFI closed at nine o'clock, and 'lights out' was at 10.30. Before this, at 9.30, the bugler would sound off, by the guard room, at the main gate. The 'jankers' brigade would then, thankfully, salute the duty officer, get back to barracks and put their battle dress away. They had all been guilty of minor misdemeanours, and they had spent the evening, since tea, on drill and fatigues before finishing the day by changing into battle dress and parading for inspection at the main gate. If they put a foot wrong, they got an extension of the sentence.

Four weeks of the primary training had passed, and our platoon was taking shape, in spite of the forebodings of Sergeant Jacks, and, to a lesser extent, Corporal Foot. We now drilled as a well-disciplined entity, and we had learned as much as was necessary, at this stage, about our small arms, 2-inch mortar and Boyes anti-tank rifle. We had done some of the exhausting rudiments of battle drill. True, there were the high lights to come, during the last two weeks – bayonet course, gas test, route march, live firing course on the range at Sealand, and then passing out. Also, there was a twelve hour guard to be mounted.

The route march went off smoothly. It was a ten mile platoon march, in battle dress, with small packs, tin hats, and rifles. It made a change to be able to march along the roads, and sing snatches of marching songs. If the songs became too bawdy, like *Bang Away Lu Lu*, or *Oh, What a Pity, She's only One Titty*, when passing through a residential area, the officer at the front, hastily called out 'March to Attention'. We would then have to march along in comparative silence until given the order, 'March at Ease'.

The gas test, too, passed off OK. We shuffled through a tear gas chamber, with gas masks on, to test for leaks. Half way through, the order 'Gas masks off' gave us a taste of what it was like to be on the receiving end of a gas attack.

The live firing course was a bit bleak. We waited about for hours, on a wind and often rain swept range, for our turn at the various firing points. It was a relief when it was our Platoon's turn to be 'butt' party, where the job was to pull down the targets, on a pulley system (from the safety of a deep trench) and patch up the bullet holes. Each shot was indicated to the firing party by a man in the trench, holding up a long pole and indicating the position of the bullet hole by a recognised signal. The rifleman was then able to see if he had got a 'bull', an 'inner', a 'magpie' (where the stick was twirled round, showing successive black and white faces), an 'outer,' or whether he had missed the target altogether. At the end of the day's firing (and it went on for a week) all paraded, with their rifles, at the rear, where boiling water was ready to pour down the barrels to clean them. The pull though was used to clean out the barrel, and the inside of the barrel was then slightly oiled, by pulling through a piece of oily four-by-two. Our rifles were then inspected by the platoon officer. Those not really clean had to be done all over again. After all, you had to treat your 'best friend' with every consideration.

There had been a minor panic, when someone threw his live grenade and it hit the top of the trench and bounced back. The other trainees of that section were round the corner of the trench, out of harm's way, but the curses of the sweating instructor, who managed to hurl the detonated grenade back out just before it exploded, could be heard all too clearly. There were many 'near accidents', but most of us survived. Sometimes limbs were damaged, and the neighbouring military hospital was never short of customers. Occasionally, the injured didn't come back to the unit, but such incidents were quickly forgotten.

There was an awful intentness about the bayonet course. We had perfected all the standing drills, and the day came when what had, hopefully, been learnt, was all to be put together, on the final bayonet assault. In this exercise, Jacks had been at his most savage. For him, no-one had run fast enough, jabbed hard enough at the Germanic dummies, or screamed loudly enough. I couldn't understand why the dummies were all so bloody big. Surely all Germans weren't six foot six, with huge, grinning teeth. The platoon had been through the preliminaries, before this final assault course. We had done the *'In, Out, On Guard!'* routine. We had mastered the Butt stroke. We had learned not to stab ourselves, or each other. We were fit and drilled. It was not easy to have to imagine ever being in the position to have to jab another man in the stomach. There had been a few cases, in the Middle East. Of course, the Russians were involved in desperate fighting, where bayonets and butt strokes must surely be the order of the day. One thing was already certain. If ever the situation arose in the future where fighting became so personal, it would be you or him. There would be no time for parley. God, the thought of a jab in the face or stomach from a German bayonet, although a remote possibility, was enough to make a bloke sweat. There was certainly no chance of a parley with Sergeant Jacks or the corporals. Do or die was their maxim.

The first four of us lined up opposite our line of 'opponents'. There was a cool breeze, but I found my palms sweating, and I was trembling. I wiped my hands down the front of my trousers. What the bloody hell was the matter with me? It was only another one of their war games. I shrugged my small pack into a new postion, and tilted my tin hat slightly forward. The top of my BD blouse was irritating my neck, where my pack straps were pulling. For some inexplicable reason, battle dress rather than denims was the order. I held my rifle loosely in front of me, waiting for the order to start. The sling was slackened off, and the old-fashioned cutlass type bayonet was fixed on the end of my rifle.

'*On Guard!*'

My rifle flew forward, into the standard position – left hand in front of the forward sling swivel, arm straight; right hand round the neck of the butt. The other three, on parallel courses, did likewise.

'*As y'were!*' '*On Guard!*'

Rifles went down and up again – more sharply, the second time.

'*Charge!*' '*Go on!*' '*Hold that arm straight!*'

I ran across the uneven ground, towards the first dummy. It was a grounded one, behind some sand bags.

'*Scream!*' '*Let's 'ear yer 'oller!*' '*Use yer bloody lungs!*'

We four ran, screaming, at our four 'victims'.

'In! Foot on his Guts! Out!' A whisp of straw hung on the sight of my rifle.

'*On Guard!*' '*Go on!*' '*After the next bastard*' '*Tucker – don't stand there admiring yer bloody 'andiwork! Private Lowson, that's not a bloody flag you've got, waving about! Hold it steady! Keep 'ollerin'!*'

Screaming hoarsely, I approached a huge 'German', helmeted, and carrying a rifle. Savagely and desperately, I lunged at the stomach. The bayonet jabbed into a piece of wooden support, and the jarring shock ran up my left arm.

'*In out! On guard! Forward!*'

I felt my tin hat wobble. I should have tightened the bloody strap!

'Come on, Private Milton – you're slowin' up. He ain't going ter sit there all day – get in first! Come on. Move!'

Another dummy had been dispatched. By now sweat was pouring off the four of us, and we were slowing up a bit. Eventually, at the end of the course, we flopped down, in line, behind some sand bags.

'Target ahead. One hundred. Five rounds. Fire! Don't ferget yer safety catches!'

I sucked air into my heaving body and blinked the worst of the sweat from my eyes. I settled the rifle on the sand bag in front and pulled the butt firmly into my shoulder. The targets became more steady, and in better focus, as the mist cleared from in front of my eyes.

'Tip of the fore sight in the centre of the U of the back sight. . .' I held my breath, for an instant, and squeezed the trigger. Working the bolt, I sent four more rounds of .303, hopefully, winging to the target.

'Unload! Safety catches on! Double away!'

Already, the next four were on their way. We who had finished filtered around the back.

Needless to say, Geoff Collard had been a bit slow, and he came in for the choicest and crudest remarks. The instructors usually 'went to town' on the Collards of any squad.

'Go on, Collard! Get a Move On! Run Collard! Imagine it's a tart, standing there, 'oldin' 'er skirt up!'

Collard did his best, although whether or not he was inspired by the sergeant's suggestion is open to doubt. The dummy fell off the hook as he flailed at it, and he extricated his bayonet clumsily.

'I don't know. I reckon she'd drop her skirt in disgust if she saw any of you lot coming.' The sergeant scowled in anger. The platoon stood about, slowly recovering wind and composure.

'Right! Five minutes smoke, and them as 'asn't got any can go through the motions,' said the sergeant.

Most of the platoon lit up. The three NCOs stood apart. Corporal Foot offered his sergeant a fag, and they too lit up and stood talking quietly. The men lay on the ground, resting their heads in the inside of their sweaty tin hats. Some had undone their webbing. Little was said. We hadn't done too badly, and the sergeant was moderately satisfied. He wasn't so bad. Some of the London boys were of the opinion that perhaps he had a mother after all.

'Right. Get fell in.' Lance Corporal Holmes came across and called the platoon to order. A pleasant fair-haired young man, who had chatted quite a lot with the lads off duty, he was nevertheless a lance jack and not a man for new boys to take liberties with. We marched off smartly, rifles at the slope and bayonets safely back in their scabbards.

'Platoon, eyes – right.' All eyes swivelled sharply to the right, and the corporal saluted, impeccably as Captain Palmer, the company commander, cycled by. He returned the salute, by touching the peak of his cap, with his cane. 'Eyes front! Left, right, left, right, left . . . left . . . left. . .'

They marched round the square and up the path, by the barrack block.

'Platoon, platoon . . . Halt.' We came to a smart halt, outside an instruction hut. 'Order arms! Right, men; fall out, into the hut,' ordered the corporal.

The other two instructors turned up. Sergeant Jacks stood at the front of the room and faced his seated platoon.

'Right, you lot. Just over a week from now I shall have to let you shower loose on the British Army. It'll be more like Frank Carnot's Army than ever when you lot get there. Middle of next week, we 'ave got camp guard. Keep yer eyes on Part 1 orders. Any man who doesn't see 'is name on orders, when it's there, or who doesn't do what it says to do, goes on a charge. Corporal 'olmes will see that you turn out right. Ev'ry man 'as got ter be perfect. We don't want no shit order in this platoon. Anything the duty officer finds wrong, and 'e'll put you on a fizzer. That's nothing ter what I'll do to yer if yer let me down. I'll 'ave yer marching yer socks off. Following day is the camp sports. This Sunday, the whole camp is marching down to the Cathedral for church parade. You'll find all the details of that in Orders as well, so watch it. Tomorrer, you've got tests, fer those who hope to go in the machine gun outfits. This afternoon, parade outside this hut, at 1400 hours. We're going fer a run. PT kit.'

We collected our irons from our rooms and were marched down to the cookhouse, section by section. There was a fair bit of grumbling. They were getting fitter and tougher daily, these city boys, and they had lost some of their pallor. But running round the roads, or anywhere else, had not been part of their lives a few weeks ago, and it still came a bit hard. A tube up West, or a bus to the 'Elephant' had been about the extent of travel. After the cookhouse, most wandered along to the NAAFI for a cup of tea. In good time, we all returned to the billet to change. At two o'clock, or 1400 hours as the military were pleased to call it, we were lined up by the hut where Jacks was waiting, complete with his bike! The afternoon 'run' was to be a bike ride for him. He set off at a steady pace, with the whole of number two platoon in full cry, like a pack of hounds. After a couple of miles of quiet roads, the field became spread out. At this stage, I was still loping along by the rear wheel of the bike, like some bruiser on a training run. With me was John Lewin, another 'out-of-towner'. We had lost the others.

'Right, you two. Turn right, half a mile up the road, follow it rarnd, and you'll get back to camp. You can get changed, and 'ave a smoke, while I go and fetch the others.'

Back at the barrack room, showered and changed, John and I had just got our beds down and were cleaning our boots, when the rest of the platoon came straggling in, cursing and blowing. While all were busy, the sergeant came strolling down the room, with a word here and a scowl there. I was sitting on the bottom of a two tier bunk when he came over and stopped by me.

24

'Private Milton, I'd like a word with you.' He spoke quietly. The others were busy changing, bed making and sprucing up. They were to be allowed out tonight. That is, most of them were to be allowed out. Collard had earned some overtime. One or two others were barred, for various reasons. Quite a few were going to a dance in town. For this we were permitted to wear shoes. We had no other civilian clothing, as all this had been sent home by the Army. The sergeant gave me a shrewd look. 'You've run before, ain't yer?' he said, rather as a statement, not a question.

'Yes, Sergeant,' I replied innocently; 'I ran in the Southern Counties, in the mile during the summer. I came third.'

'I thought so. Well, keep yer marf shut! Don't you tell nobody. Understand?' Mystified as I was, I shrugged in acquiescence. I had already learned that you don't ask too many questions, no matter how odd the order sounded – especially if the sergeant gave it. If that was what the sergeant wanted. . . I put it out of my mind, and decided that I might go to the dance. I hadn't got a lot of cash left, but enough.

A few of us set off for the main gate, buttons and badges polished, everything as it should be. Successfully negotiating the route through the guard room, and having signed out, Bill Smith and I set out down the town. We picked our way through the old part of the city, turned left into Station Road, and pushed our way into the hall, where the twice weekly dances were held. The room was not very big, and fairly quiet. The dance group of drums, sax, trombone, double bass and piano, was grouped on a low platform. The soldiers, forage caps tucked into shoulder lapels, stood inside the door and sized up the situation. They were mostly soldiers, with a few civvy blokes. Most of the women were local girls. A few of them were sitting primly along one wall. There were still traces of french chalk on the floor. The night was young, and things hadn't really got going. Bill and I were tempted to get a pass out and go for a pint, but money was short, so we hung on. We were both passable dancers. I had been to a little establishment outside my home village, where I had been shown the rudiments by a martinet of an old dancing instructress. What Bill hadn't learnt, he could make up for by sheer city confidence.

After the end of the waltz, *When Irish Eyes are Smilin*, the dancers returned to the chairs, or to the sides of the hall. After a pause, the group struck up the next dance. I looked along the row of girls, and picked out a pale but quite pretty one, a year or two older than me. I took a breath and went up to her.

'May I have this dance, please?' I asked, with as much confidence as I could muster.

Dutifully, she rose and followed me on to the floor, where the quickstep had started. Confident at least of my dancing, I led my

25

partner round, in a fairly orthodox fashion. As she responded well to my firm lead, I became more ambitious, and spun her round with vigour, whenever space permitted. This she appeared to enjoy, althoug she clutched her skirt to prevent it billowing in too unseemly a manner. The compère called the end of the number. I thanked her, and then felt a bit at a loss. Without speaking, she went back to her seat by her friend. I walked over to Bill, who was by the door. 'Ow d'yer get on?' he asked, gruffly.

'OK,' I replied, with more confidence than I felt.

'Take your partners for a slow foxtrot,' called the compère. The band struck up a familiar tune, and a few confident couples made a start. After a decent pause, I walked across to my partner of the previous dance. 'May I have this one, please?' I asked. She passed her handbag to her friend, and again joined me on the floor. I guided her round to the slow rhythm of the foxtrot. My firm lead made it easy for her to follow, and we were able to negotiate a circuit without undue disturbance. I held her right hand with my left – being careful not to hold her hand up too high – a common fault with tall men, so I had been taught. My right arm was firmly round her waist. She kept her head turned to one side, as I steered her round. 'Do you come here, often?' I asked, wondering what was the best opening gambit.

'Most Thursdays, with Freda,' she replied.

'Oh, that's your friend,' I replied, inanely.

'Yes, we work in the same shop, up in the Rows,' she said.

'D'you live in the town?' I asked.

'We live out at Seaton,' she volunteered. 'We get a bus, or, sometimes, a taxi.'

'What's your name?' I asked boldly.

'Joyce,' came the short rejoinder.

'My name's George,' I said, feeling stupid. God! How do you make progress with one of this sort? What sort was she anyway? Most of the soldiers were looking for an easy bit, and most of the girls who went off with a strange soldier surely knew this. The town was full of good time girls, coming in to live it up in the evenings. Many of them were prepared to risk a one night stand. The alleyways and doorways would be littered with couples in tight clinches when the dance was over and the pubs turned out. I knew only too well that the victories of the night's encounters would be acclaimed in barrack blocks and wooden huts, or recounted over a cup of NAAFI tea tomorrow. Again, at the end of the dance, I saw her back to her place, and then went and re-joined Bill. The evening wore on, and Bill, who was getting fed up with the place, decided to move on. With his greater experience, he had weighed up the situation, and found it wanting. He had already decided that there would be 'nothing doing', as far as the girls were concerned, but I wasn't too keen to move. Bill decided to leave me to it. 'You'll find out,' he said. 'Even if you split up those two, you won't get far with that one you've tagged on to.'

Finally, the group struck up the last waltz, and there was a bit of jockeying for position. Those who had been 'nursing' a prospect all evening, claimed their partners. It was understood that the bloke who saw a girl home would be one whom she partnered for this dance. I had taken the plunge, against the better judgment of Bill, and I was dancing with Joyce, clinging closer to her as the floor became more crowded. I could feel the straps under her blouse with my right hand, and her head rested on my shoulder. I was already irresistably drawn into an inevitable course of action. I would see her home – it was only a short bus ride to her village – and Freda had already promised herself to a young Cheshire, whom, apparently, she knew.

'Can I see you home, Joyce?' I had cast the die. My voice sounded far away, and I felt stupid.

'If you like,' she replied, off-handedly, with her head over my shoulder. I held her a bit more possessively, and felt a bit light-headed. This was new ground; I had never spoken to a girl, with intent so to speak, before.

The band struck the last, drawn out note, and couples drifted off the floor.

'I'll get my coat; I'll be back in a minute,' she said, as I led her towards the door. She disappeared into the 'Ladies', with a sprinkling of other girls. I waited. I began to wish that I had gone for a 'leak' when I had the chance, but it was too late now – I was frightened of missing Joyce. I hung about with the other escorts, feeling a bit 'spare'. I put my forage cap on, and waited trying to look at ease – as though this was something that I did often. God, she was a long time! Several of the other girls who had gone in at the same time, came out and departed with their male company. Suppose she had gone. Suppose she was having me on, and had crept out by some other exit. Suddenly, she was by my side, having apparently materialised out of the air. She looked a bit different with her outdoor clothes on. I took her arm, awkwardly, as we went down to the bus stop, where we waited a few minutes for the bus. It was a double-decker, and we climbed on to the top deck. It was crowded. We had to sit separately, as the bus swayed and jerked its way out of town. I had not been this way before, and I was looking out of the window, so that I could find my way back. I knew it wasn't far. The conductor came clumping up the stairs, jingling the change in a bag strapped round his neck.

'Any more fares, please.' I paid sixpence for the two tickets, and the conductor moved on. Joyce indicated that I had paid for her ticket. After a stop or two, the bus thinned out a bit, and I was able to move up and sit next to her.

'It's the next stop,' she said. The bus squeaked to a halt as she pressed the bell, so I stood up and led the way down the staircase. We got off, and I could just make out the dim outline of a row of houses, showing as a shadow in the blacked out street. It was very dark. She took my arm as we walked up the lane. Too late, I realised what a twit I had been.

'What time have you got to be back?' she asked, knowing bloody well that I hadn't got any time.

'Twenty-three hundred hours – I mean, eleven o'clock.'

'Oh, I see.' She stopped by a gateway. 'This is where I live,' she said.

'I stood awkwardly, bursting for a run out. 'Well, I shall have to go,' I said, 'it's going to take me till then to get back.'

'What happens if you're late?' she challenged.

'I'd get put on a charge,' I replied. 'I'd get jankers – wouldn't be allowed out for a week, and be made to do a lot of drills and fatigues till bed-time.'

'Well, you'd better get back, then,' she said, tartly. 'I must go in, or they'll wonder where I am.' She pushed open the gate, and closed it after her. 'Goodnight, then.'

I stood there, for a minute. Christ, I was going to have to run. I started to trot along the road, back to town, hoping that a bus would overtake me. None did. The road was dark, and I bumped into the kerb. Sod it! I was going to have to put a shift on. There was no traffic about, and I started to run, steadily, up the middle of the road. I felt much better since I had been able to relieve myself in the hedge, as soon as Joyce had disappeared. I felt a bit unbalanced, running in my shoes. It was surprising how soon you got used to Army boots. I could just see the outline of the hedges on either side as I pounded along with my shoes clip clopping on the road. I saw the approaches to the town, and I sped through the now deserted High Street, and out the other side into more familiar country. I was on the road back to camp. Already, it was twenty to eleven. I loosened my collar, and stepped up the pace. Striding out briskly, I saw the faint glow from the camp guard room at last. I was OK! The sentry by the entrance saw me coming, so he did not waste time challenging me. 'Hurry up, mate, you're cutting it a bit fine,' he muttered.

'I put my cap on and did up my collar. I walked into the guard room. The sergeant looked up at the clock meaningfully as I signed in.

'Hope she was worth it,' was all he said.

The agility tests took place next day. We started with the usual hustle in the ablutions. About sixty men had to share wash basins, of which there were ten. There wasn't a lot of time to spare in the mornings, and it didn't pay to be last in the queue. Today, the water was cold, as it often was on other days, and shaving was made that more hazardous. Bill Smith managed to push in next to me.

'Ow d'yer get on?' he asked.

'OK,' I answered, trying to sound as though I meant it.

'Did she come across, then?' Bill was nothing if not to the point.

'Wasn't really time,' I said, airily. 'I did alright, though. Wasn't even time for a knee trembler. Anyway, I might be seeing her again.'

'I reckon you were on the wrong one, there,' said the voice of greater experience. 'I reckon 'er mate would 'ave bin a goer. She would 'ave let you 'ave it, if you 'ad chatted 'er up a bit, first. That other one looks as if she kept it at 'ome. 'Ad a mouse trap up there, shouldn't wonder.'

The agility tests were simple. The recruit had to rush around, within the prescribed time limit, transferring rings from one set of pegs to another. The pegs were set round on a piece of ground behind the training huts. It was rather like playing some parlour game at a party.

Postings came up, on Part Three orders, next day. This was the first parting of the ways for soldiers who had lived together for six weeks. Mostly, the platoon was split between the Middlesex and the Cheshires, with a few going to the RNFs and the Manchesters. Some were going to rifle regiments, and they would be posted away. For the machine gunners, it simply meant a march across the camp with all their kit, less rifles, to their new regimental lines. One or two were being moved out to the quieter waters of RASC or RAOC. Even Geoff Collard had got by, in spite of his awkwardness, and he was going to the Middlesex.

On Friday night, the platoon mounted its much rehearsed guard – from 2000 hours to 0800 hours. On Friday morning, Jacks had seen me and told me that I had been taken off the guard rota. I was a bit puzzled by this, but he added that I had been entered for the mile race in the annual camp sports, to take place next day.

'You'd better win, too,' Jacks had said, darkly. I knew that sport was taken seriously in this outfit, but I was rather mystified. Why should it be so important that I win the race? The centre boasted a cinder track, and the whole garrison turned out to watch the events. I knew nothing about the opposition in the mile, but I wasn't very worried. I felt pretty confident, having been trained to concert pitch for this very distance during the summer. The race was four laps of the track. I had no real plan. I just intended to follow whoever was leading for about three laps, and then take it on the fourth. The race went entirely according to plan, and, after trailing round, for a rather slow three laps, I took a comfortable lead in the fourth, and won easily.

It was some weeks later, when I had joined the regimental training company, that I discovered the real significance of my late sergeant's concern. The two previous years, the race had been won by a corporal instructor, from HQ company. Jacks, with typical old-soldier shrewdness, had made ten shilling bets, all over the sergeants' mess, and he scooped a windfall. A training sergeant had dropped a few hints, when he found out who I was. Needless to say, I didn't get a percentage, and I often wonder what would have happened had I lost the race.

The church parade was the first big parade that we new boys had been on. Up to now, we had moved about at platoon strength. Now, we were to assemble at battalion strength. We dressed for the part, and we lined up for an initial once-over, by Corporal Foot. He straightened a collar here, set a cap right there. The order of the day was best BD, boots and gaiters. The boots were a dull black – they were all dressed with dubbin, as an anti-gas measure. Sergeant Jacks had a few words to say before handing us over to our platoon commander, Lieutenant Childs. We were assembled and marched, smartly, round to the square. Here, we were fallen out and allowed to wait along the side of the parade ground. Numbers one and three platoons were already hanging about. A company of RNFs had just arrived from another corner, and they were soon joined by the other three companies and the HQ company. The men of the four regiments proudly wore their highly polished cap badges and their shoulder flashes. The fearsome figure of RSM Jones, of the Cheshire Regiment, took over. The RSM was not a man to be trifled with, and those assembled, or most of them, lived in awe of him – even the junior officers. With a raucous voice, untuned by years of shouting on parades, he addressed the gathering.

'R-ig-hT Markers!' At this order, one chosen man, from each platoon, snapped to attention, and marched, briskly, on to the square to a pre-arranged spot. 'Left, right, left, right! Swing those arms!' The right markers all duly arrived, and stood to attention. John Lewin was right marker for number two platoon. A level-headed lad, he had been chosen by the sergeant, and his smart turn out and military bearing showed that that trust had not been misplaced.

'Bat'n!' All the men at the sides of the square, stiffened. 'Battal-ion, Git on parade!'

Someone in each squad, softly called out the timing.

'Shun, two, three, Left, right, left, right. . .' Each platoon formed up to the left of its marker.

'R-i-g-h-t dress!' Right arms, fingers curled, shot out, sideways, and heads swivelled to the right. With briskly shuffling feet, they dressed on their marker.

'Ey-es front.' Arms shot back down to the sides, and heads

swung back, into position. The RSM about turned, with a stamp of feet, and marched across to the camp commandant, Colonel Pearson. His arm jerked up, the longest way, in a perfect salute.

'Battalion on parade, sir!' A few more words and salutes were exchanged, and then the colonel took charge.

'Fall in the officers,' he commanded. The officers, who had been assembled near the CO, came to attention, and marched smartly on to the square, taking up the appropriate positions, with platoon commanders in front of platoons, and company commanders in front of them.

'Battalion will move to the right, in column of threes; Battalion, r-i-g-h-t turn.' Almost as a man, the battalion snapped right, so that the platoons were now in column, one platoon behind the other, company by company. The officers took up new positions in front of their platoons. The band of the Cheshires had been assembled in one corner. They now struck up a regimental march.

'Battalion will march off, number one company leading.'

'Number one company, quick march!' The commander of the RNFs marched his men off behind the band. In turn, the other companies tagged on, with the primary training company bringing up the rear.

It was a bright, fresh morning, as the marching column, headed by the band, swung through the main gate – a thousand men behind their colonel. Such traffic as there was had been halted by the regimental police, and the splendid cavalcade crossed the Liverpool Road and set off for town. The locals lined both sides of the road, and children skipped along, keeping pace with the soldiers. Older men looked on, silently and critically. Many of them had experiences of this nature, in some previous camp, in some previous army. They knew what they knew, but their faces showed no emotion as they stood around in small groups, watching the latest army pass. No doubt, these boys would be able to give a good account of themselves when their time came.

Church over, the companies re-formed in the cathedral square and marched back to camp. As we marched past the onlookers, I felt a surge of pride. There was something satisfying about being even a small cog in such a well-oiled machine.

The afternoon was our own, but there was to be a kit inspection in the evening, prior to postings, and there was little time to spare. Kit had to be laid out meticulously, in a prescribed manner, to be inspected by the eagle eye of the company commander, Captain Palmer, and the quarter-master-sergeant. Any deficiencies in kit had to be paid for.

Even in the trying days of October 1942, a passing out parade was still a momentous event, especially for those taking part. Again, turn out had to be perfect. This time, the dress was battle dress, with rifles and webbing belts. Anklets, belts and rifle slings were carefully blancoed, and brass fittings meticulously polished – care being taken to see that no polish smeared the webbing. Rifles were clean and perfectly oiled. Even the studs on the boots were looked at to ensure that each boot contained its thirteen polished studs. As for the church parade, our company assembled on its right markers. This time, however, we brought our rifles to the slope before marching on to the square. The band played in the background, while Colonel Pearson walked along the ranks, carefully inspecting each man for smartness of equipment and neatness of person. He walked slowly down the ranks of number two platoon, followed by the company commander, Captain Palmer, the RSM and the RQMS. As he came opposite to me, I felt the colonel's piercing eye scrutinising me, from top to toe, and back to top. I felt naked, and waited for some defect to be detected. The colonel moved on, and I felt a relaxation of tension in my shoulders and in the back of my legs. After the inspection, the companies marched past, platoon by platoon, whilst the band played. On coming level with the figures on the rostrum, each platoon was given the order, 'Eyes right,' by the platoon commander, who, himself, saluted.

That was it. There only remained the unexpected invitation, made by Sergeant Jacks, to the platoon to join him and the corporals, in *The Royal Sceptre* that evening, for a few pints to round off the primary training. From now on, we would belong to a regiment, and we were to set about the important task of becoming soldiers, real soldiers!

Chapter Two

Sergeant Jacks was thirty-seven, and so, by infantry standards, he was an old man. He had grown up during the First World War, in which his father had died – one of the millions of khaki figures lost on the Somme. His mother had died soon afterwards, from TB, and young Fred ended up as a Barnardo boy. He had no real complaints: he had been well cared for, but he felt the need for institutional life, and after several unsatisfactory jobs, he ended up in the Army. He had done well. After serving a hard apprenticeship in India and Egypt, and having lost half a finger, the result of a ricochet from a tribal bullet on the North West Frontier, he was sent on a weapon training instruction course, and so found his way to the 24MGTC, where he had the unenviable task of knocking these recruits into shape. He had learnt a lot about recruits and their problems. He realised that it was a traumatic experience, coming from a sheltered home, or an East End community, into the war time army. He should know. He himself was an East Ender, who had grown up in the back streets, around Stepney. He had learnt to be a survivor, but he had a certain sympathy for these youngsters. He had to be hard – after all – these were hard times, and the Army had to turn out good soldiers in a desperately short space of time. The Army was the sergeant's life – he had known no other – the Army had been mother and father to him. Here, he had found good comrades and a sense of purpose. Even so, he appreciated the problems of the civvies. To them, he was a fearsome mentor – not inhuman – but certainly not quite like one of them. In fact, there were a number of recruits who had good cause to be grateful for the sergeant's humanity, when there had been problems at home. Jacks was a bachelor, but he was 'father' to his squad. He would brook no bullying and he would brook no idling. His corporals respected him. He was hard but fair. He had, however, a certain curious regard for the Collards, Miltons and Lewins of the platoon. He respected their brains and education, and he was extra pleased when they responded to the situation that they found themselves in, hardened up and fitted in.

No doubt he would soldier on in this capacity until the end of the war. Eventually, he would be 'time expired', and then he would return to London, in some job or other.

Having just seen this six weeks' programme through, he would have a few days leave. After that, the next lot arrived, and he and his corporals would start all over again, bringing another intake on, and sending them off to the regiments, with a few of the corners knocked off.

About two-thirds of number two platoon had reached the required standard of agility, height and weight, to join the support regiments, where they would now learn to handle the Vickers .303, medium, water cooled machine gun, as well as the dreaded 4.2-inch mortar.

The machine gun was the mainstay of close support. It was a sturdy, solid weapon, and it had to be carried considerable distances by hard-trained sections of men. It travelled in two parts, the barrel mounting – the gun itself – and a tripod. The crews had to learn just everything about this gun, and it took several weeks of gruelling training. With the battalions, it was usually transported in Bren-gun carriers. These were highly-manoeuverable, open, tracked vehicles, capable of about 40 m.p.h. on roads, and very useful across country. Each carrier was manned by a driver NCO and the machine-gun crew of three. Twin Vickers were sometimes mounted on 15 hundredweight trucks, and used, quite effectively, against low-flying aircraft.

Very often, the machine-gun was fired at an unseen target, from just below the brow of a hill. The .303, specially adapted Mark 8Z ammunition had a range of about 4,500 yards. Under these conditions, the guns were layed by the use of a lensatic sight, and the curvey trajectory took the bullet over the hill. Fire was often directed from an observation point, when messages were relayed to the gun by telephone or radio. Sometimes, firing was by 'map shoot'.

Close support meant that the guns fired close – very close – to their own infantry; on their flank or just to their front, to protect them from enemy fire. The curtain of support kept the enemy with their heads down until they found themselves assailed by the advancing infantry. Anyway, that was the theory, and that was one of the roles of the MMG. Mistakes in laying the gun for support fire were rarely made, but they could be very costly.

The section leaders and the platoon sergeants had a reverance for the guns, akin to that found among artillerymen. The gun itself was an interesting piece of mechanism. It was belt fed from the right, and it was kept cool by a metal water jacket, surrounding the barrel. The hot water convected round and into a can, fed by a rubber tube. It reminded me of the liebig condensers that I had used in the labs. It had a fairly complicated 'lock' mechanism, which was part of the return or recoil system. A gunner had to know his gun in all its moods. When a stoppage occurred, he had to be able to remedy it, and quickly, too. His life, and the lives of the troops he was covering, depended on his skill and speed. His was a job requiring fitness, speed, physical and mental agility, and, of course, courage. Machine gunners were not popular with the enemy, and when their position was detected and became untenable, they had to be able to dissemble the gun, and MOVE! Often, this would mean pitching it, and themselves, rapidly into their 'carrier', during the few seconds that the vehicle came up from the rear, and departed again. The ammunition belts were carried in wooden boxes, and were brought up, as required, by number three. Number two fed the belt in, from the right, and looked after the can of water, linked by tubing, to the cooling system. A skilled number one could 'tap' his gun, to within half a degree, when changing the lateral line of fire. Of course, every man in the team could do every other man's job.

In each support battalion, and there was one of those in every infantry division, there was, also, a company of mortar men. The 4.2 mortar was a much more recent addition to the weaponry of the British Army. This, also, was a hard task master. It fired a twenty pound bomb up to something over 4,000 yards. The bomb was, essentially, a blast weapon, and it had a thin case, full of explosive. It was a terrible weapon, with a devasting effect on the lungs of enemy infantrymen. It was also carried in special vehicles – half tracks – and it had to be fired from behind a protective ridge. Once its position was plotted by the enemy, it brought down their maximum wrath, and then had to be moved, quickly. It, also, came in two parts, a base plate, weighing one hundred and twenty five pounds, and a barrel, weighing ninety pounds. These loads often had to be man-handled over rough country – at speed.

These, then, were the two main weapons of the support regiments. Besides this, the soldiers had to be infantrymen, able to use all the usual small arms, and to be proficient in infantry battle drill. Many of them were also trained as wireless operators, line and signal men, drivers, first-aiders, builders and engineers. Each man had to be versatile, so that he could play his full part in a crisis. Two mortar bombs were carried in a metal case, and they too, had to be humped over rough ground.

Chapter Three

Hut twelve was a large, black-board building, with a pitched roof. At one end was a small room, used by the senior corporal. The door was in the centre of one side. The hut was on short, brick pillars, and had a wooden floor. It contained twenty double bunk beds. These were clumsy, wooden constructions, with fixed, wire frames. In the centre of the hut, was a closed coke stove, with a metal stack pipe, leading up, through the roof. Round the stove was a concrete hearth, and standing by it, was a coke bucket. By the door were two, red fire buckets, containing sand. The corporal in charge would come out through the connecting door, to stir the inhabitants for parade, or to check for tidiness. There was only one way to leave the bedding and kit – the right way.

Six of the old number two platoon had been marched round to the door.

'When you're dismissed, you can get in there, 'jilty', and get yerself an empty bunk,' said the corporal, 'then get straight back out here.' We found ourselves unoccupied beds – I got a top bunk, down towards the end. When we had reported outside, again, we were marched away from the hut, down a gravel path, on to a main, concrete track. We were then taken to a store hut of some kind, in the corner of the regimental area. The corporal produced a key, and undid a padlock. He then issued one cotton palliasse, one pillow case, of similar material, and four brown, or grey blankets, to each man. In the corner of the hut was a large heap of straw, and I thought this to be a stable of some kind.

'Right, pack your mattress and pillow case with straw,' ordered the NCO, 'but don't fill 'em too full, or you'll roll off 'em.'

We stuffed the straw in, through a hole in the side, and then laced it up. We were then shepherded back to the hut, and told that we could make our beds down, before tea. I looked at my miserable bag of straw. This was a come-down. This bag of scratch straw was not going to be as comfortable as the three 'biscuit' mattresses, we had left behind in primary training. The bed looked pretty uncomfortable. The hut was rather dark and gloomy, and some of the windows were masked by high bunks. There were no lockers, and all spare kit had to be stored in your kit bag, and stacked by the side of the bunk.

''allo, mate; just come over from PTW?' asked a soldier, who had surfaced from some corner of the hut.

'Yes,' I replied, 'I'm just getting me bed down, before tea. You the only one about?'

'Yeah,' replied the stranger; 'They're out, on gun drill, but I got a bad foot, so I'm left behind, to look arter the billet. Dropped a bloody tripod, and busted me toe.'

'I don't reckon much to this bloody bed,' I said, miserably; 'I shouldn't wonder if this bag o' straw weren't full o' fleas.'

'Nah, it's awlright,' said the orderly, with a laugh. 'When you make it, put plenty of blanket underneath. You'd be surprised; you get as much cold from underneath, as from on top. An' lap the blanket over, like this, one thickness over another. That way, yer get no draughts coming in, and they don't end up on the bloody floor.'

I was grateful to that room orderly. He showed me how to layer my blankets and so make the best of a bad job. The rest of the new boys had gathered round my bunk, and they all had the good sense to take note of what was going on.

The hut started to fill up. The squad had been on gun drill. They were tired and ready for tea. The afternoon had been dull and chilly. Not that the hut was particularly cheerful. It was not yet cold enough for the stove to be lit, and the lights could only be put on when the blackout boards were in place. Some of the more energetic ones had already nipped out to the wash room, and some were climbing out of denims and boots, and into battledress and shoes. One or two were shoe shining; some were lying, flat out, on iron bed springs, with their heads propped on a stack of blankets. We newcomers were not wanted until next day, but first we had to parade, for tea. We were marched down to the large, central cookhouse, swinging our right arms, and with our left arms behind our backs, our left hands gripping our 'irons' – knife, fork and spoon. Tea over, we walked, briskly, back to the hut, in twos and threes.

We new boys spent that evening settling in. We had been issued with red cloth infantry bars, and these had been sewn on to our tunics and greatcoat by the tailor. We had our new cap badges to shine, and cap and overcoat buttons to clean.

With a few of the older hands, we sat on bottom bunks or at the trestle table and got on with our various chores. Some of the lads were writing home, to parents or girlfriends. I had written my letter home, to my mother and father. I always wrote to the two of them, although it was my mother who did all the corresponding for the family. My father was a skilled craftsman, working on aircraft components. My brother had started work, at the end of the summer, for the firm that I had just left, and he helped to keep some of my old mates, in the picture.

Bill Smith had just finished darning a sock. This was a job which had to be done carefully, because bad darns caused blisters, and the nastier types of Army boss could call a blister a 'self inflicted injury'.

He gave a grunt of relief, as he put the grey wool and the needle away in the 'husif' (housewife). This was just a small cloth pouch issued to all soldiers, and it contained cotton, needles and wool. All simple repairs had to be done by the men themselves. When items of clothing were really past it, you could present them to the RQMS on a clothing parade. The chances of his giving you a new replacement, were about fifty-fifty.

'Hey, George, coming down the NAAFI, for half an hour?' asked Bill.

'Yeah, OK,' I replied, looking up from a button sewing job. 'I want to post this letter to my Ma, and we might as well go for a tea and wad.' I stuck down the letter that I had left on the table and dug a stamp out from my pay book. Pay books were always carried in the left hand tunic pocket. This was the soldier's identity card and had to be produced at the request of any appropriate military person or the civil police. The NAAFI was some way from our new quarters. We made our way through the Middlexsex and Cheshire lines, past the sergeants' mess, round the side of the square, and into the canteen.

''Allo, darling. Can we 'ave two cups of char and a couple of Chelseas?' said Bill. The NAAFI girl poured two teas from the urn, and put two cakes on a plate.

'I'd better 'ave a bar of soap, too,' I said, and dug into my pay book for a soap coupon. The room was not very full. We stayed at the counter, 'chatting up' the girl. She was new, and younger than the others. Her face was flushed with steam and a whisp of fair hair escaped from the front of her cap.

'Ain't sin you 'ere, before,' said Bill, as an opening.

'No, I started yesterday,' she replied; 'I've just finished my week's training.'

'Where do you come from, darling?' asked Bill.

'Tarporley,' she replied; 'it's not far away. I can get home weekends, when I'm not on duty. I expect you two are from London.'

'Yeah, more or less,' agreed Bill.

'You don't come from London, do you?' she went on, looking at me with curiosity plainly showing in her blue eyes.

'No,' I said, awkwardly; 'I don't come far from there, though – place called Slough.'

'Oh, I've heard of it,' she exclaimed, 'don't they make Aspro, there?'

'Yes, and Horlicks and Mars,' I answered.

'How long have you boys been here, then?'

'Oh, we're old soldiers,' grinned Bill. 'We've just done our first day in this mob.' He pointed to his cap badge. 'We just done our first six weeks.'

She sighed.

'Cheer up,' went on Bill; 'you'll be able to go 'ome on Saturday, an' give yer boy friend a cuddle.'

'I haven't got one – well,' she qualified, 'I was sort of going out with Pete, who lives next door, but he's in the RAF, and he's somewhere down in Kent. What about you boys?' she went on, but looking hard at me, 'I bet you've got girls.'

'Not us,' said Bill, stoutly. 'Perhaps we might take you an' your friend out fer a dance one night. We both trip the old light fantastic.'

'Mmm, that might be nice, when I've got a night off,' she agreed, but giving me what might be called a pensive look.

I suddenly felt embarrassed. 'Come on, Bill,' I said, suddenly, 'we'll collect a few cups up.' We went round the tables collecting empties and bringing them back to the counter.

'Thanks,' she said. 'My name's Sue, by the way.' She poured us two more teas from the urn and waved away Bill's half-hearted gesture to pay. Having swallowed our second cup, we stood around while Sue served a couple of RNFs who had just arrived. When she had finished, she came back to where we were standing and leant her arms on the counter.

'Where's your billet, then?' asked Bill.

'Just down the bottom of the road,' she replied, promptly. 'There are several of us in a brick hut. It's out of bounds to you fellers.'

'Never mind darling, we could always pop along when it's nice and dark,' quipped Bill.

We said goodnight and promised to sort out a date when the girls had a free night. We stumbled back in the dark to Hut 12. Bill carried on a rapid patter as we picked our way through the lines.

'She fancies you, George,' he said, enviously; 'you'd do alright there if you nursed it along a bit. Cor, she was giving you the eye alright. If she's got a nice cuddly mate we could be well in there. You wouldn't 'ave ter rush it, mind. She'd be a bit scared, I reckon, and you'd 'ave to talk 'er round a bit – tell 'er you'd be careful, and nothing could go wrong. But you get 'er on the right night an' you could lift 'er skirt alright. Put it in for yer, I shouldn't wonder.'

'You reckon,' I murmured. I was, it seemed, rapidly coming face to face with a new aspect of life in the Army. 'I don't reckon there's anything there,' I went on, with an ill-placed show of worldly wisdom; 'she don't know what it's for. She just wants someone ter take 'er to a dance, or the pictures.'

'Oh, yeah. Like I said; you'd 'ave ter chat it up, a bit,' said Bill, and then went on to embellish on the matter; 'she wouldn't drop 'em straight away, but she fancies you, mate.'

We made our way back in the dark. There was a faint glow showing from some of the huts as we passed. We called in at the latrine for a last pee, and went in to the hut. There was not long to go before 'lights out'. The nights had turned really chilly, and like most of the others, I spread my greatcoat over the blankets for extra warmth – a habit that has carried on over the years. I had got used to 'the rough, male kiss of blankets', now. I remembered the line from Rupert Brooke about blankets and having to write an essay on the odd things that I liked · a pale imitation of Brooke. I remembered writing about the smell of tar, of new mown hay, and of the orderly rows of potatoes, as seen from a road at the edge of the field. I had seen plenty of 'orderly rows', in the last few weeks. I wriggled down between my blankets. I was wearing my army angola shirt, and 'drawers, cellular'. There were no pyjamas or sheets for the private soldier in 1942. Some of the boys wore their grey socks in bed, but they tended to make my feet sore. I settled down. Gradually, others crept in to the hut, trying to get settled in before the lights had to go out. The occupant of the bunk below me had come in, cursing, but he soon got organised and settled down. One or two others were talking softly in one corner, where someone was cautiously using a flash light to find his way to bed – cautiously, because the black-out boards had been taken from the windows. One of the late entrants had had a few beers, it seemed. He crept up to a sleeping form on the next bunk to me. He walked with exaggerated caution, looking ludicrous in his shirt and drawers. He gently shook the recumbent form.

'Hey, tosh.' The form stirred slightly, and grunted.

'Come to bed, Paddy, you stoopid barstard,' mumbled a sleepy voice at the other end of the hut.

'Hey, tosh.'

The form grunted. 'What? What's 'at? What d'yer want?'

'Wan' er buy a battleship?' asked Paddy, urgently.

'Piss off, you stoopid sod!' The form turned over. Paddy gave an inane hoot, and was persuaded back to bed. Somewhere on the other side of the hut another squaddy let a rasping fart.

'Check, paste up, back to five hundred,' murmured another.

The hut settled down. There was the rise and fall of snoring – some of it pretty heavy – due, probably, to a belly full of beer. I was tired all right, but sleep didn't come easily. I lay there, while exotic visions flashed up on the screen of my mind's eye. The 'inward eye' that was supposed to be 'the bliss of solitude', was not giving much bliss tonight. First, there was Sue, lying in some meadow, gently acquiescing, while I boldly eased her NAAFI overall and underlying petticoat up to her waist, showing a strip of white thigh, between her stockings and her knickers. She was sighing in ecstasy as I put my hand up, and she parted, gently, as she helped me with my fly buttons. I fell asleep, and eroticism invaded my dreams. I saw the trooper, with the girl by the river, accomplishing his task, while the girl looked at me and smiled, sadly and mockingly. I dreamed of Joyce allowing my wandering hand to unbutton her blouse and caress her breasts. She wore a tight, knowing smile – knowing me for what I was, and knowing that I would be beaten by the curfew. I dreamed of Freda, her friend, kissing me passionately, and guiding me to my goal, delighting in having some part in my education.

I woke up suddenly, feeling uncomfortable, but relaxed. Freda had been too much for me. My fantasy passions had exploded in an ejaculation – a 'wet dream' – and I felt embarrassed and miserable. I cleaned up as best I could, and fell into a dreamless sleep.

My awakening was rude. The corporal from the end room, was on early duty, and he was up and about on reveille.

'Come on, Wakey, Wakey!' He went down the centre of the hut, shaking the bunks. 'Come on, you lucky lads! Rise and Shine! Come on, now. Hands off cocks, on socks! Outside, in five minutes, in PT kit.'

The cookhouse orderly had brought in a bucket of tea, and they lined up with pint mugs. Then they were away. Round the camp roads we clumped, in singlets, shorts, boots and socks. 'Left, right, left, right, left. . .' We soon warmed up, although the morning air was chilly, and the fields were hardly visible in the thick, rising mist. We completed the circuit of a mile and ended up outside the billet, 'double marking time'. We fell out. Some scrambled for a wash basin, to procure one for an early shave, while some got on with bed making first, waiting until there was room to shave. At 07.30 hours, we were marched off to breakfast, of porridge followed by bacon and tomatoes, and tea. The food was good, and very adequate, although the trainees were always hungry. As infantry soldiers, we were on special supplementary rations, and better fed than the rationed civilian population. But our programme was physically very exacting, and we burnt up all our bodily fuel.

The days and weeks that followed were to be a long round of square bashing, weapon training, lectures and field craft. Apart from further instruction and tactical exercises, in the small arms that we had been trained on initially, we were, now to be introduced to the Vickers machine gun. Our first morning continued with an hour's square bashing, taken by Sergeant Brooks who had made a speciality of drill instruction. While this was going on, another group had been marched off to the machine gun training area.

I was with the drill squad. The drill was tolerable. Sergeant Brooks had managed to sharpen up the squad no end in a few days. His executive word of command came over as a sort of stifled scream – very effective! The platoon reacted as one man. The company sergeant-major had been watching from the side lines, and he seemed moderately pleased. CSM Benton was a large, cumbersome man, not without bluster. He bludgeoned his way through his military duties, and although generally efficient in a brutal sort of way, he certainly lacked the human touch. Like many senior NCOs his promotion had been accelerated by the rapid expansion of the wartime army. In many cases, educational tests, normally required for sergeant and above, had been waived for the duration, and senior NCOs, sometimes found themselves entangled in parade states, equipment and ration returns and training programmes before they had undertaken all the necessary courses.

After drill, we returned our rifles to the hut and had a five minutes' smoke. Then we were marched down to the training area. The rest of the morning was spent on lectures and demonstrations of the working of the MMG, in a hut on the training area nearby. Facilities for MMG training were shared, and our platoon met Sergeant Taylor. Sergeant Taylor was a Londoner, but he was in the Cheshires. He, like Jacks, was minus a piece of finger. This seemed to be a traditional wound of a machine gunner, like duelling scars for regular German Army officers. He was quite a reasonable character, with a sense of humour. He was also a good, patient instructor.

The Vickers was a complicated piece of machinery. It seldom went wrong, but there were quite a number of ways in which it could. The rest of the morning was spent learning the stoppages, and the general working parts.

In the afternoon, section by section, we got down to it. Three at a time, we were detailed as gun numbers. Number one sat behind the gun. Number two lay down, on his right, and fed in the dummy rounds in the belt, while number three lay down in the rear with spare ammunition and water. Instructions were shouted, by corporal instructors.

'. . . carry on firing . . . gun fires a few rounds, and stops again . . . ease, pull, tap and carry on firing . . . ! Right, change! Change again! And again!'

On the order to change, number two became number one, and they moved round, in a cycle.

This would go on for hours.

The weather had turned colder, and often the drills would go on in driving drizzle. Flopping down on the muddy ground became more miserable as winter set in. When you weren't on the gun, you were observing. Sometimes the remainder took up positions, with rifles, and went through the motions of supporting the machine guns. Sometimes they did all this wearing respirators.

It must have been hard for the instructors too, but we trainees thought only of our own miserable lot. We cursed the camp, we cursed the NCOs (in their absence), we cursed the Army. But, progressively, we became sharp and confident in our ability to handle the gun – the gun around which our waking hours seem to revolve. Of course, we hadn't fired it yet. Later, much later, we would be operating with other units on tactical exercises. However, that was a long way off.

Physical fitness and mental alertness were keynotes of training, and there were few let-ups. Myself, I very much looked forward to sessions in the gymnasium with the qualified PTIs. These came in two kinds – there were the professionals – the man of the Army Physical Training Corps – always sergeants or above, and usually men whose civilian jobs were professional sportsmen, or they were specially trained regulars; and then there were the local, regimentally trained instructors, who were corporals. The gym sessions were very similar to P.T. lessons at school and involved the usual rope, beam and box work. However, the physical bug-bear of the week was the Saturday morning cross country run, of just over five miles. This took place every week throughout the winter, whatever the weather. It involved all the fit men in the camp below a certain age. It was started by a word of command, and the huge mass of runners would then set off from the sports field, and the keenest of them would jockey for position before reaching the first bottleneck, the gate into a field. There were penalties for the more dilatory. Anyone who came in behind the camp commandant, Colonel Pearson, earned a Saturday afternoon extra PT with the instructors. The more who failed to make the grade, the more were the instructors who had to give up Saturday afternoon; consequently, the instructors tended to work out their frustration upon the luckless victims, and they made the afternoon a very exhausting one. Colonel Pearson was much older than the other runners, but he had run for his county – Cheshire. Normally, I had no worries whatever about the run; in fact, I enjoyed it. On one recent Saturday morning I had come second, and I hoped that I would manage to win the event before I was posted away.

My undoing came, partly as a result of my keenness to win the event on a Saturday, partly through the vagaries of the system, and, partly because of the lack of imagination of CSM Benton.

One Saturday in my second week in the hut, I woke up feeling under the weather. I had not been out for a drink – I was always careful on Friday nights – but I felt hot and ill.

'You look a bit rough, George,' said John Lewin; 'd'you feel alright?'

'No,' I replied, 'I feel bloody rough. Anybody'd think I'd been on the piss, but I didn't even bloody well go out last night.'

'Go bloody sick, George,' chipped in Jim Dodson, 'you don't look too good, mate.'

'No, bugger it,' I mumbled, 'I'll be OK, when I've had a mug of tea. If I go sick today, bloody MO'll think I'm skiving – probably give me M and D, in bloody red.' I carried on making my bed up and getting ready to go to breakfast. 'Anyway,' I went on, 'It's too much bloody trouble. I got to get me kit in store, an' pack me bloody small pack, before I can go.'

'Yeah, bloody stoopid,' said Jim. 'You got ter be bloody fit ter go sick in this outfit!'

There was some truth in what he said. To discourage malingering, or fussing over minor aches or pains, the Army had made it quite a difficult task to report sick. If you 'tried it on', and the MO gave you a 'chitty', saying M and D (medicine and duty), but written in red, it was a warning to your platoon sergeant that the doctor considered that you were skiving, and then the sergeant would take appropriate steps. Things were to change in later years, but these were the rules in 'A' training company, when I woke up that morning feeling 'rough'.

After breakfast, and when it was too late to report sick, I lay on my bunk watching the room spin. John Lewin was worried. He was a sensible lad, and it was pretty obvious to him that I was not any way fit to run in the cross country at eleven o'clock. It was a typical damp and chilly winter's morning. He looked for the hut corporal, but he couldn't find him. He went along to the company H.Q. hut, hoping to find somebody who could help. Their platoon sergeant, Sergeant Dent, had been sent home for the weekend, on compassionate leave. John walked into the office and found the orderly clerk typing some leave forms.

'What can I do for you, mate?' asked the private orderly.

'Got a mate who's sick,' said John; 'want ter find somebody who can give him permission to stay in his bunk, instead of running, s'morning.'

'Why didn't he bloody well go sick, then?' asked the orderly, who was excused today's run to be on duty.

'I dunno. He's got worse, since he got up, anyway,' added John.

'Well, here come Comny Sarnt Major,' said the orderly. CSM Benton walked into the office.

'Excuse me, Sir. Private Milton is not very well, in our barrack hut, and I've come to see if someone will give permission for him to be excused the run this morning,' went on John.

'Has he got a chitty from the M.O.?' asked the warrant officer.

'No, Sir, he didn't go sick,' replied John.

'Well, there can't be much wrong with 'im, if 'e didn't go sick,' came the answer. 'If 'e 'asn't got a note from the M.O., then he's fit to run. If he's not there, he'll be on a charge, Monday morning,' replied the sergeant-major, adamantly.

'But he's pretty sick, Sir,' replied Lewin, worriedly, 'I think he's got a temperature'.

'He'll be alright. I expect one of the old soldiers has been teaching 'im a trick or two; piece of soap, I shouldn't wonder. Off you go.'

'I don't think . . .' wavered John.

'That'll do, Private Lewin – 'tis Private Lewin, ain't it? It's no good, sending you along to try it on. Off you go now, or you'll be late for the run.' The sergeant major brought the interview to an end, by going into his room, and closing the door. The orderly looked at John, and shrugged his shoulders.

On the 'off', the mass of runners shot across the field. This time, I wasn't in the first bunch. My legs felt heavy, and my breathing was all wrong. On going through the first gate, I found myself already gasping for breath, and more and more of the runners streamed past me. Soon, I found myself down among the escorting PTIs, yapping at the rear, urging the flock forward – acting like bloody sheep dogs. My head swam and my face burned. My legs became heavier and the insides of my knees knocked together, making a bruise. I staggered on round, pumping my arms to try to keep some rhythm. However, half way round, I was sick. For a few minutes, things seemed easier. I wondered, vaguely, if I would beat the deadline, but I was past worrying about that; it just didn't seem to matter. I got round, and without waiting for any 'inquest', lurched along the concrete paths, through the camping lines, up the gravel path, to hut 12.

I slipped on the steps, fell forward, thumped my shoulder on the door jamb, and fell. There I lay, draped across the three wooden steps leading in to the hut. Dimly, I could hear voices through the half-open door. The rest of the platoon had returned and were getting ready for dinner, prior to 'going into town in the afternoon.

'I lay there, with the hut, the grass and the sky, seemingly changing places. I couldn't get up – my legs had packed in. I gave a last, desperate groan, a bit louder then the last one.

''ere, what's that.' The speaker was the soldier who had broken his toe, and who had shown me how to put my bed together when I had first arrived.

'What's what?' asked Bill Smith.

'I dunno; I heard a bloody moan.' He went to the half-open door. 'Bloody 'ell,' he exclaimed when he saw me draped across the steps, 'what's the matter with you?'

Someone else came across. 'Christ, it's George,' said a voice. By now a couple more inmates had come to the door. One was John Lewin.

'Jesus!' He looked at me in alarm. He saw my flushed face and stertorous breathing. 'Are you all right, George?' he asked. Then it became obvious to him that I was not alright. 'Give us a hand Bill.'

Three of them manhandled me into my bunk. By now, the hut corporal had turned up. He looked worried when he saw the state that I was in. By now I was feverish, and I was muttering and calling out, but not apparently making any sense. That was enough for Corporal Brown. He shot straight along to the MI hut. Inside, an orderly was sweeping up and a lance-corporal medic was filling some bottles.

'Where's the MO?' asked Brown.

'Don't know, corp. Officers' mess, I expect.' The medic looked up from his task.

'Fetch him along to hut 12 – I've got a sick man there.'

'Well, I dunno, corp.' He looked dubious. 'He won't want to be disturbed. It's dinner time.'

'Bloody well fetch him – quick! I'm going back to the hut,' said Brown, and hurried out.

'The inmates of hut 12 stood around in a silent, slightly awe-struck group. The doctor came in. They were called to attention by Corporal Brown.

'Alright, carry on,' said the MO, testily. 'This man, corporal, what's his name?'

'Private Milton, sir,' relied the NCO.

The MO came over, and looked at me as I lay, muttering, in the bunk, and pulled out a thermometer. 'Carry on, man; snap out of it!' he commanded, while fitting a thermometer under my tongue. I felt a wave of weak rage sweep over me. He thought I was skiving after all. He felt my pulse. Then he took out a stethoscope from his case. The man had tucked me under some hastily laid down blankets, and I was still in singlet and shorts. They had taken my muddy shoes off. The corporal pulled my singlet up while the doctor prodded, back and front.

'Hmm,' he muttered, 'just leave him there, corporal, and I will send for him.' He packed his instruments, gave a casual salute as Brown called the men to attention, and he was gone.

'Bloody awright,' said Bill, in disgust; 'bloody pig-headed Army. Bloody sergeant-major ought to have known better. 'Im and 'is bloody rools and regulations. Look what's 'appened, now.'

'I expect he'll be alright,' said John Lewin, 'now he's got to go to hospital.'

'I lay on my bunk, only half aware of what was going on around me. The fellers stood around in groups, or quietly got on with shoe cleaning or button polishing, ready to go out. After about fifteen minutes there was the clatter of a vehicle drawing up, and a door clanging open. Voices were heard, and in came two medics with a canvas stretcher. They were shown my bunk and I was soon humped on to the canvas. John Lewin, on the instructions of the corporal, had packed my small pack and some clothing, and the rest of my equipment was stacked up to be taken to the company stores. The doors of the ambulance closed with a clang, and I was driven off, leaving my mates of hut 12 to relax tension and get on with the business of Saturday afternoon.

The ambulance drove the short distance to the hospital, next to the camp, and I was carried in. I remember thinking that it must be a bit like a ride on a camel, and I wondered, strangely, if I should end up riding a bloody camel in this man's Army. I was given a wash by a girl nursing auxillary – I was still muddy from the run – and I was put into bed at the end of a long medical ward. I was aware of pyjamas – the first for weeks – and a tall, slim QAIMNS nurse, who came and went on several occasions.

It was never made very clear to me just what was the matter. I was certainly pretty sick and sorry, for a while. However, conditions in the military hospital weren't at all bad. I was in a comfortable bed, with sheets and a mattress, and I was wearing pyjamas. The room was warm and cosy. True, I did feel a little awkward when I found that the nurse in charge ranked as an Army officer, and so was far senior to me. However, for all that she was kind and pleasant. The VAD nursing auxillary, who was on day duty, was about my age, and she chatted to me as my condition improved, and when time allowed. Ten days after admission, when seemingly I had been at death's door, I was discharged back to the camp. I was, however, given a certificate by the MO, allowing me 'light duties' until the following Monday, when I would probably be back on full training.

I walked back to camp and reported to the company office. I was seen by the same orderly who had talked to John Lewin on the morning of the run. The orderly looked at me. He got up out of his chair and moved towards a door at the end of the office. His voice could be heard inside. 'Excuse me, sir,' he said, 'Private Milton's just returned from 'dock'.'

Sergeant-major Benton came out from the inner office. He frowned when he saw me, and I hastily stiffened to attention, when he addressed me.

'Ah, you're back then, Private Milton.' Private Jones, put Private Milton on today's ration state and parade returns.'

'Yes, sir,' said the orderly.

'You're fit now, are you, Private Milton,' he asked, pompously.

'Yes, sir; I'm alright. I was told to give you this.' I handed over an envelope from the hospital, which included my sick note and another note. I then noticed that the envelope had not been sealed. The CSM took the envelope with a grunt. He looked at the medical certificate, and passed it on to the orderly. The note, he kept. I had not thought to have a look in the envelope, so I didn't know much about the contents.

'Right, Private Milton. You are on light duties until Monday, when you must report sick, before the MO will clear you. Until then, you go to lectures, but for the rest of the time you will be hut orderly. You are confined to barracks until you are cleared, on Monday.' He made it all sound as though it was my bloody fault that I had been ill. 'You had better get along to the c'mpany stores and get your kit. You then go along to your hut and make your bed up, properly. And see that the hut is kept tidy. I shall be coming round to 'ave a look.'

'Yes. Thank you, sir,' I said, thankful to escape. I collected my kit and took it all back to the hut. I changed into denims, and sorted the kit out. I then carefully cleaned and oiled my rifle. There was a letter from my mother on the bed. I tore it open and read it while sitting on the bottom bunk, below my own. I had written to say that I was in hospital, and my mother's letter was full of concern, heightened by lack of adequate details of my trouble. I gave a sigh and set about writing in reply, so as to allay their groundless fears.

Just before the end of the morning, Corporal Brown came in. He was on his way through to his own small room when he saw me. 'Hallo,' he said. 'Back, then. Everything OK?'

'Yes, thanks, Corp, I'm alright,' I replied. 'I'm supposed to be on light duties, 'till Monday.'

'Just as well,' he said, with a wry smile, 'you'd soon find yourself knackered on runs and drills. 'Be surprised how soon you get out of touch. Anyway, there's a platoon run, in FSMO, this afternoon, so you won't be on that. There's no need to spend all the time in the hut. If it's clean and tidy, you can 'ave a mooch round the camp and get some fresh air. You mustn't go out of camp, though.' He gave me a thoughtful look. 'You caused quite a stir, round 'ere, I can tell you. I shouldn't be surprised if somebody 'asn't dropped a clanger – more than one, quite likely. So, just be a bit careful, an' keep yer nose clean. If I were you, I'd keep my head down, fer a few days – keep out of the way.'

'Thanks, Corp,' I replied, reading the ominous warning implicit in his remarks.

The rest of the boys came staggering in. They looked pretty tired. Apparently the square bashing and the gun drill had been more than usually arduous. 'Cor, 'ere's George,' came a cry.

'Watcher, George.'

'What the nurses like, George, you lucky sod!'

'Any of 'em 'old yer 'and, in the middle of the night?'

'Oooh, nursey, nursey; come an' 'old it for me!'

'Did she give yer a barf, then?'

These and a number of other quips were flung at me. The lads were obviously pleased to see me back. I was one of them now, even though I wasn't a Londoner, and as far as they were concerned, I had been given a bad time.

We were formed up and marched off to the cookhouse. John Lewin and Paddy sat next to me.

'Alright, then George? You sure look a lot better than you did, last time I saw yer. Thought you were going ter turn yer toes up, mate,' said Paddy, as he shovelled down baked beans.

One or two others, sitting round at the table, asked me how I was – some of them, inevitably, made lewd suggestions about the nurses.

Paddy leaned forward across the table. 'There's bin a right old rumpus. I 'eard someone say that the CSM 'ad 'ad a bollocking over you. I 'eard that 'e 'ad ter go an' see the Colonel. They thought you was going ter be a lot worse than you was.'

I carried on, shovelling baked beans and soya links into my mouth. I felt a bit embarrassed, and a bit foolish. Christ, what was going to happen to me? After all, I should have gone sick in the morning, and so got excused from the run.

'Bloodly silly,' said John Lewin. 'The CSM knew you weren't swinging the bloody lead – after all – you nearly won the bloody race, not long ago. 'Been different, if it had been Paddy; they all know he's a lazy, bloody sod.'

It seemed that there had been some sort of 'inquest' about the whole affair. I heard no more about it.

On Monday I saw the MO, and, to my relief, I was put back on full duties. I soon got back into the groove. As Corporal Brown had said, you soon got soft, lazing about, and it only made life harder in the long run.

Chapter Four

Leave! True, we were getting only a forty-eight hour pass, but still, it meant going home. I felt surprisingly thrilled. After all, I had come here partly to escape. It would, I realised, be great to go off for the weekend and see Mum, Dad and brother Brian. I hadn't missed them most of the time. Certainly, I had felt sorry for myself on a few occasions, and I had sat in the hut, or hung around in the YMCA Club in town on a Sunday afternoon, moping and dreaming of what I might have been doing if I had been at home. I shouldn't have been doing anything very exciting anyway. I might have been helping with the garden chores – gardening was quite a serious business with my father – the surrounds of our three-bedroomed house had to be neat and tidy, and the vegetables had to be as good as, or better then, any others in the village. I might have been struggling with some impossible maths problem, set as a result of my night classes. During the previous summer I had been involved in a few athletics meetings, and I had done quite well on the track. After my last triumph, in the mile, my father had talked of my joining a 'more fashionable' club, and 'taking it up'. Anyway, I had taken it up now alright! I got to thinking about the other lads in the platoons. It must be bloody hard for them. After all, I had found it tough, and they hadn't spent the summer like I had. How they spent their Sundays, in the East of the City, I did not know, although I had listened to them talking about 'The Market' and 'the dollies' and the various clubs and cliques that had been part of their lives. Already, they were surprisingly fitter. They smoked and drank, when they could afford it, and they cursed and joked about their lot, but there wasn't much that could crush them.

There was a general stir of excitement in the company lines. All those who were of the same intake as me, and who had, therefore, got in about ten weeks' service, were being sent on leave. Passes and travel warrants would be issued from company office, about 1600 hours on Friday (said Part 1 Orders), and train times to London were published. All those going were to be inspected at the Guard Room, and no one was to be allowed out until he had passed muster. As it was only a weekend leave, rifles and full kit would not be taken; rifles were to be put in store and kit left in rooms. Respirators, small packs and tin hats had to be taken.

There wasn't much done, from Friday midday. Those who were going on leave were a bit tensed up. This was, after all, the first leave, and they had been away from home for some weeks. At dinner time, I went along with a bunch of London boys to a hut further down the company lines. Apparently, one of the platoon had a mate there who wanted a message taken home to a girl friend. Soldiers wandered around – along the paths, and in and out of the huts – in various dress. The strains of *Tangerine* came from an ablution. We visitors looked in to one of the huts.

'Where's Chas?' asked one of my party, ''allo, Chas.'

Chas was sitting in the doorway, smoking. He stubbed out his dog end.

''Allo, Tosh,' he greeted. We sat around the step. The others engaged in general chat – mainly about the instructors, or the girls in town. Suddenly, a slight, auburn-haired Cockney, who was cleaning a pair of boots, broke into loud and raucous voice. The words of his ditty were so crude and unfunny that I listened with a mixture of awe and amusement.

Oh, Good Morning, Mrs Wood;
Is a sprarzie any good,
For a sniff
Of yer old, jam roll!

The last line was bawled out. There then followed a horrifyingly disgusting second verse. The other lads just grinned, and left the soloist to it.

Business completed, we went along to the NAAFI. I saw Sue, serving a long line of soldiers. She gave me a distant smile of recognition, and got on with her job. I thought about trying to make a date – to fix something up for when I came back from the weekend; but there were too many squadies about and I felt I needed Bill's support to make a foursome.

I put my kit into store, made sure that I was correctly dressed, and went along to the office to collect my pass and travel warrant. The Army didn't usually give travel warrants for weekend passes, but this, being our first, was an exception. I clutched the precious piece of paper and went along to find Bill. Quite a few of the boys were going to London, on the 5.15 train. This meant that there wasn't too much time to hang about.

Four of us marched along to the guard room. The sergeant on duty inspected our passes, passed us as smart enough, and let us go. We waited for a bus to the station. We were lucky. We had got off to a quick get-a-way, and the bus was not too crowded. The double-decker drew up at the station with a squeal of brakes, and we scrambled off and into the entrance. The train was in, and we marched along the platform.

'*The train standing in Platform 3 is for Crewe, and London, Euston. Passengers for London, occupy the front three coaches*'. The Tannoy blared at us as we hurried along. We got in at the end of a carriage and walked along the corridor, looking for a suitable compartment. The best we could find was occupied by a sergeant in the REs and an old lady. We crowded in, and dumped our kit in the rack.

After much hissing of steam, shouting and banging of doors, the train got going with a series of shudders and jolts. The sergeant opened one eye, saw nothing to interest him, and closed it again. The lady read a magazine.

Before long the train steamed into Crewe. Here there was a long wait. Eventually, after much shouting and shunting, our part set off for London. The train was crowded. The corridors were full of troops, standing, leaning on the windows, looking out at the darkening, Cheshire landscape. There seemed to be an endless procession of soggy fields, hedges and farm buildings, with occasional roads striking out to nameless villages and hamlets. I decided to take a walk down to the lavatory at the end of the corridor. I picked my way over packs, kit-bags and cases; I squeezed by soldiers sitting on their kit, and made my way to my destination. Anyway, one trip down the corridor should see me through. I fought my way back to my seat. The old lady closed her magazine and looked at the young soldiers with dulled eyes, glancing casually at the regimental name tapes on their epaulettes. It was dark now. Fortunately, the train was an express, with few stops. It was hurtling along, at a fair pace, with sparks and smoke whipping away into the night.

The men said little. Paddy was squeezed in next to me. He said something about 'Lil', hoping that she would be available in her usual Hammersmith haunts, and on form. He said he hoped he could do her justice and not be spiked by the bromide in his tea. It was commonly supposed that the Army tea was dosed with potassium bromide – meant to depress the urges of fit and lusty young men. Paddy lapsed into silence.

Eventually, a series of lurchings and rat-a-tat-tats of the rail network, signalled the approach to Euston. Over-anxious, many of us were kitted up, with caps on and necks done up and warrants clasped in blanco-smeared hands, long before the station. The train slowed. The beginnings of a platform sped by, and the train came to a halt, well forward and a long way from the ticket barrier. We straggled off and hurried along the platform, with sketchy farewells to each other. MPs, impeccably turned out, with red caps down at the regulation angle and arm bands slightly below their tapes, hovered around. By the barrier were two full corporal MPs, one on each side of the gateway, carefully scrutinising the troops and their warrants, as they passed through. Streams of humanity poured down the road to the Underground, and diverged, to various platforms, from above, down into the caverns, reached by escalators.

There was already a large crowd on platform three, waiting for the Uxbridge/Hounslow trains. Along the sides, by the glazed walls, civilians were bedding down for the night, in family groups with young children already tucked in. Flasks and tea cups were being passed round, as housewives valiantly tried to cope with this new and horrifying method of catering for the family. The sight saddened me. Suddenly I became thankful for my lot, safe in an Army training unit, while these City dwellers faced appalling difficulties and very real dangers.

The first train in was for Hounslow. After an ever increasing rumbling and crashing, it appeared at the mouth of the tunnel, and ground to a screeching halt by the platform. Some got out, and many poured in. The tunnel went quiet again, and some bits of paper swirled in the stiff breeze from a gust of forced air.

Here it was at last! The 'Uxbridge' destination label was blazoned across the front. I found myself standing in a bad spot, because the nearest set of double doors rumbled open some distance away. The waiting crowds poured in so eagerly that those alighting had considerable difficulty.

I stood in a crowded carriage, one hand on a roof strap. My small pack was between my legs, with my tin hat strapped on the front of it by webbing straps.

Stations came and went with their names appearing faintly through the gloom. As we left the City and came out to the suburbs the passengers began to thin out. Some got on at each stop, but more got off. Eventually, I found a seat and sat down, with my pack between my feet. The carriage became emptier. A neat looking girl with doe-like eyes sat opposite and gazed blankly at me. Eventually, she got off at Rayner's Lane. Where was she going? Who would meet her? Probably some lucky bugger would be taking her out later. Idly, I surveyed the remainder of my fellow travellers and took to guessing what sort of people they were.

Finally, we reached the end of the line, and the few of us left got off and made for the barrier. The solitary ticket-collector waved me through, without inspection, and I hurried out to catch the last bus. I caught it, and paid my fare to the wandering conductor – the travel warrant didn't stretch this far – and settled down on a bench near the door. There was no one who recognised me. I knew the rest of the journey so well. I got off, and walked the last half mile. The garden gate and the drive were so familiar I night have been here yesterday.

I opened the door and went in, through the darkened kitchen to the living room. The wireless was off, as the compulsive news bulletins had gone.

'Hello, mate,' said my mother.

'Hello, Mum, Dad,' I said, casually. My father looked up from his arm chair, his reading glasses on his forehead.

'You made it, then,' he said.

'Yes,' I replied, to the obvious. 'The Underground was packed.'

Brian, aged sixteen, looked at the uniform and the pack with some awe. My mother gazed at me carefully, looking, I guessed, for signs of my recent hospital spell.

'You all right, then? We were worried when you wrote from the hospital,' she said.

I took off my tunic, exposing my army pullover.

'You look tired, George,' continued my mother, 'I'll put the kettle on for a cup of tea.'

My father gave me a quizzical look. He too had been in the Army, just after the last war, and he knew something of the life, although he had not been an infantryman.

'What's it like, then?' he asked, looking for any sign of wavering or lack of spirit.

'Oh, it's alright,' was all I could say; 'It's tough. They don't 'arf chase us about – but it's OK.'

'Blimey, they've straightened you up, a bit,' he observed cryptically, as I stood up to find my pass and show them my Pay Book. I could see that he was quite impressed, although he usually tried hard to play things down. I certainly had filled out a bit, and I suppose it showed more, in the pullover. My mother came in with some cups of tea on a tray. She had also found some bacon and egg. Although I didn't feel particularly hungry after the hustle and bustle of the London stations, I realised that it must have meant some sacrifice on their part to produce this, with the rationing on.

'Right – thanks, Mum,' I said, and got on with it. They had made up a bed in the little spare room. This was the room where I had spent so many hours studying, first for my school certificate, and then for my London exams, for which I had had to work in the evenings. Well, that was all behind me now.

We sat up quite late, while I told them something of my life in the Army. It seems I spoke with animation, and it became obvious to my father that I had accepted the life, and even appeared to be enjoying much of it.

The next morning, I got up quite early. My father had gone to work. My mother had some office job in an aircraft factory, but she had insisted on having this Saturday morning off, saying that her son had been in hospital, and that he was home on his first leave. I found that I could not stay in bed. I put some old clothes on, and wandered downstairs. The vegetable garden had the derelict look that gardens have before winter digging is done. It was a crisp, dry morning. I wandered down to the garden shed and fetched the fork that was always used for digging. I took off my jacket and found my old boots. Before long, I had dug out a trench and was well away. In a couple of hours the increasing area of neat, level, turned soil, gave me a deep sense of satisfaction. I paused for a breather. Mrs Rogers, our next door neighbour of some years standing, had come out into her garden.

'Hallo, George, home on leave, then?' she said, when she saw me over the fence. 'How'ya getting on, then?'

'Alright, Mrs Rogers,' I replied, 'I've finished my primary training, and I'm in the regiment, now.'

'Oo, dear! Does that mean you'll be going abroad, soon?' she asked.

'No,' I laughed, 'I've got a lot more training to do yet.'

'When are you going back?' she asked.

'Oh, I catch a train from Euston tomorrow afternoon,' I said, wondering why people always have to ask you when you are going back. 'I shan't get in 'til pretty late, and I'm on a training run at 7 o'clock on Monday morning.'

'My goodness. They're either trying to toughen you up or kill you,' she went on. 'I must tell Jim you're home; he would like to have a chat with you, being an old soldier himself, like.' She paused, then went on, 'Your Mum says you were in hospital – quite worried she was, at the time. Are you better now?'

'Yes, thank you,' I replied.

I got on with my digging. By dinner time I had done a really good stint. At one o'clock my father came home from work, on his bicycle.

'Blimey,' he said, when he saw the extent of the digging, 'It would have taken me a month to have done that.'

After dinner of sausages, known at camp in these rationed times, as 'bread in battledress', I changed into uniform, put on a pair of shoes instead of my boots, and went up the road to see John, who was about my age and was talking of joining the Navy. John was no great pal. He was not really my type, but we met occasionally, and we had spent some time together during school holidays. John was a bit of a loner, and he had not joined in some of the outdoor pursuits, like tracking and scrumping, that had been so much part of our lives, as boys in the village. John had not gone to the same grammar school as I had, but to another one, further off, at Marlow. I talked about life in the Army, and John went on about some of the jobs that he had to do in the labs of the engineering works where he worked. It was a way to spend an hour or two, talking to someone from the past, in the peace and quiet of John's garden.

After tea, I felt restless – I had a bursting desire to get out. I caught a bus into Uxbridge, and had a pint in *The Three Tuns*. I was in the local regiment, and my flashes created a little interest among some of the older locals. Later on, I looked in at the Saturday dance night at Burtons. Dancing partners were not difficult to find, and I enjoyed the evening. I had danced with the same girl several times, so I escorted her home, said goodnight, and then walked home. The walk seemed shorter than it used to be. I was not particularly late, and they were still up.

My mother had packed sandwiches for my train journey back, on Sunday. I had shared their rations for Sunday dinner, but they had managed quite well. As it got nearer to the time for the bus to take me to the station, I felt a certain strain developing between us all. My leave had been short, and a bit unsettling. I was glad to see everybody, and, of course, they were delighted to see me, but now it was time to get back and pick up the threads again.

Chapter Five

The camp was settled, when we got back. Our passes were inspected by the guard sergeant, and we made our way to hut 12. Our beds had been made up for us by our hut mates. We all crept in to bed. My mind rested on the events of the weekend for a few minutes, then I fell asleep.

By the time we had done the morning run, now a bit later because of the dark mornings, and exchanged details of the weekend, we were back in the groove and might never have been away. Paddy had met his Lil over the weekend, and they had, it seemed, had a heavenly time. As a result, they had, according to Paddy, sworn undying allegiance to each other, and he was going to be a sober and reformed character. Even I, green as I was, realised that this was a hopeless quest, and one that would melt away after the sun had set very few times.

Not long after this, Bill and I went to the NAAFI early one evening. 'We might get a date with those birds,' said Bill. We had walked through the company lines, and we were approaching the entrance from the side, when we saw the NAAFI girl, Sue, and a friend, coming out of their hut, all dressed up.

'Crikey! There they are, George; it's their bloody night off,' exclaimed Bill. He gave a shout. Sue saw them. She looked undecided, then gave a faint wave back. It was just then that I saw the two Cheshires coming round from the other side of the club. They joined the girls, and all four made off, arm in arm. Bill looked a bit sick.

'Ah well,' he said. 'They found somebody to take them to the pictures, like you said. I don't suppose they'll get nothing.'

Even so, we both felt a sense of 'let down', and we decided to go to town to drown our sorrows.

We went back to the hut, and quickly changed into battle dress.

'We'll 'ave a look in *The Jolly Boatman*,' said Bill. 'Its this end of the town, and I expect they'll 'ave a sing song in there.'

We trudged through to the outskirts of the town, and came to the door of the pub. It was already pretty full, but we pushed our way in.

'Look who's here, then,' said a voice from a table in one corner of the saloon. Seated against the wall, on bench seats, were two or three lads from the Cheshires who had been in number 2 platoon with us at the beginning.

Bill got two pints, and we wended our way over to the table to join the company. There was a fair old crowd of them, occupying the whole corner of the room. A number of local girls were with them.

We joined the party. The evening was still young. The room was crowded with service men and local girls. There weren't many civilian fellers about, as the pub was the one nearest the camp and was considered to be the servicemen's local.

Pete Drage was a Cheshire who lived locally, and he knew most of the girls. The lads tended to talk about their Army life, and tried to outdo each other with tales of horror about the training, and the monsters who had charge over them. Bill's graphic account of my collapse and sojourn in hospital, became the number one dramatic tale of the evening, and brought 'ooh's' and 'ah's' from his absorbed female audience.

'Well, he doesn't look so bad, now,' said a girl alongside me. She was fair-haired, with blue-grey eyes, and it was apparent that she possessed a trim figure and a slim pair of legs, even though she was sitting down.

'Oh, he's not so bad,' said Pete. 'We used to have some fun at PTW. Good runner, is George; he won the mile, at camp.'

'Oooh, he's a bit fast, is he,' giggled a chubby girl by the blacked-out window.

Pete laughed. 'He's alright, Bet; don't you go upsetting him.'

I gave a weak grin. I could sense my fair-haired companion glancing at me with a sideways look.

'I expect you're a bit of a lad, like the others,' she said.

Bill gave a choking sound as he swallowed his beer. 'He's a devil when he's roused,' he said, lugubriously.

'Yes, that's right,' I said.

The evening was going with a swing. Pete had got a round in. He was better off than most of us, as his old firm was quite generous, and sent him some cash each month to supplement his pay. He had just received his quota for the month. I was later to find that my old firm, an international combine, was going to send me half a crown, by postal order, each Christmas that I was in the Army!

'What did you do, before?' My companion had put her glass down close to mine, and our hands touched, briefly, giving me a tremor, which seemed to travel up my arm and down into my stomach.

'By the way,' interrupted Pete, with mock formality, 'George, meet Stella; Stella, this is George.'

'Ole George is a brainy boy,' said Bill. ''E used ter work in a posh job all day, and go to night school at night – 'e's done ovver fings, too – an' 'e's not 'ad much time to spend with the ladies.'

'Oooh, what a waste,' said Pete's girl friend, Jean. She was his regular – he had known her before he joined up – and although young and lively, she was content to be a 'steady'. She liked Pete a lot, and she knew that time was limited; he would have to go somewhere – sometime.

'Have you a girl friend, George?' Stella had returned to the attack.

'No,' I replied, in some confusion. 'Like Bill said, I never really had any time.'

'Oh well,' said another girl, with her arm round her man's neck, 'you'll be able to make up for it, now you're here.'

'What kept you so busy, then?' Stella was on the offensive.

I went on to explain a little about my job in the research labs where I had worked, and how I had helped to produce paint for industry and for the war. This was the first time I had talked to anyone on this topic since I had joined the Army, and it was some comfort to find a interested and ready ear.

'I should have thought you would have been reserved,' said my fair companion.

This was getting a bit personal. 'Yes, but I got fed up with working,' I said, unconvincingly. 'Anyway, I used to have a barney with the old man at home, so I joined up.'

'Yes, but surely you could have been in something else,' she went on.

'Why?' I said, defensively, 'I get on alright with this lot, most of the time.' I felt a bit embarrassed. I hadn't been quizzed like this before, about my motives for being where I was. My mind went back to the day I had come home from the recruiting centre at Acton. I had been there all day. I had passed the medical, opted for this lot, been sworn in, and been given 'the King's shilling'. There had been some upsets when I got home. My father, resigned to the fact that I was going, had banked on it that I should join some technical corps. I had come home in the evening, and broken the news. To my alarm, my mother had started to cry, and I had crept off, out of the way. The younger fellows, at work had regarded me with some awe and envy the next day. The older ones had given me some pitying, 'you daft bugger' looks, thinking that I had had a sudden rush of blood to the head. The seniors in the firm had been rather annoyed.

'I told yer 'e was a brainy bleeder,' said Bill, breaking my reverie. He was paired off with a sultry looking brunette, and he seemed very content with the way the evening had developed. We all chipped in for the next round. Bill and I went off to the gents.

'OK?' said Bill. 'Don't know where they live; we may 'ave ter split up, so I'll see yer, back in the 'ut. She likes you, George. I'm alright, wiv Josie. She knows 'ow many beans make five.'

We threaded our way back between the tables of drinkers. Stella watched us coming over the rim of her raised glass. She was weighing me up, that was obvious. I had been a perfect gentleman all the evening – mainly because I was too shy to be anything else with a girl like her, and I was a bit different from the infantrymen she usually came across in the town. I was not so rough and ready as the ones she saw – hardened young men, many of them – especially the southern boys, from the London area. She knew that they could be rather a wear. They usually expected a girl, met in a pub, to submit herself to their fierce, groping hands, and to satisfy their desperate urges, in some darkened alley, or spread out under a bush by the river. She was looking at me while I was arguing with Pete about some silly incident that had happened weeks before in training, and I was aware that I was making a very favourable impression. The stories that had gone around that evening had helped to add to the intrigue and attraction. My atheletic prowess had been mentioned, as had my job. Also, it was obvious that I was shy, as it was rapidly becoming obvious to me, that she had got me in her sights.

The party was breaking up. It was a crisp, dry November night. The darkness was enhanced by the rigid blackout. We straightened our uniforms and stamped our trousers over our anklets. After all, this was a military town and there was no sense in inviting trouble. The pairing off had sorted itself out, to everyone's satisfaction, and we all left. Mostly we were travelling in the same direction – back into the city, and, north – by the station. Once outside the pub, she slipped her arm through mine and held me, with an intimate proprietorial squeeze, holding my hand as well. I felt a surging glow of pleasure. No girl had claimed me in quite this way before, and it gave me an odd feeling of 'belonging', of being wanted. I suppose this was mixed with some pride, because she was the most attractive girl in the party.

Conversation was in snatches, and a few gusts of laughter could be heard from those ahead. Stella slowed down a little, so that we became separated from the others. She gently released my arm, and drew it around her waist. I turned my head towards her, and she leaned up, and kissed me lightly, on the lips. Emboldened, and still primed with dutch courage, I drew her into a dark corner. She had half expected this, and was prepared to be kissed. It was soon obvious to her that I was no expert, and, I expect, she felt that she could handle any problem I could pose. She gently drew away, and took my arm.

'Come on,' she said. 'It's getting cold.'

Suddenly, at the end of a cobbled alley, we came on two houses, making the end of the street.

'Here we are,' she said. 'Thanks for bringing me home.'

I felt suddenly awkward and desperate with an ache in the pit of my stomach – an ache that I had know before, once or twice recently, when confronted with this sort of situation.

60

'Perhaps I can meet you tomorrow,' I stuttered.

She gave it some thought. 'We could go to the flicks, couldn't we?' she suggested.

I was slightly taken aback. I had not expected events to take quite such a promising turn.

'There's a good film on at the Odeon,' she went on. 'Bob Hope – I think he's ever so funny – Oh yes, and I'd like to pay for myself, she added, hurriedly.

'Sure,' I gulped, 'What time?'

'Why don't you come here and pick me up? If you are a bit early, my Mum's alright – she won't bite. I ought to warn you, though, she's Pete's auntie.'

Events were certainly moving more quickly than I had expected. 'Would half past six be too early?' I asked.

She laughed. 'If I'm not ready, you'll have to talk to my Mum. Well, I must go, now, George, I don't want to be late for work tomorrow – and what about you? You mustn't be late.'

'OK, see you tomorrow,' I agreed. As I moved to go, she pulled my head, gently but firmly, to her, and gave me my first real lesson in kissing. As I parted my lips in response to her more expert performance, I felt myself being drawn more tightly to her, as she pressed with her left hand on the back of my head. Her tongue came forward, caressingly, and her body pressed hard against me.

'Goodnight, darling,' she said, and with a click of the latch, she was gone.

I wanted to shout out! Instead, I ran like a maniac, back up the alley, along Station Road, and into the High Street. I felt exhilerated. I raced furiously up the road. Suddenly, at the edge of the town, I was confronted by a flash lamp.

'Hold it, son!' There were two civilian policemen at the corner. I stopped. 'What's your name, then? You seem in a bit of a rush.'

They came up close and shone the light on my shoulder flashes.

'Oh, you're on your way back to camp, eh?'

'Yes,' I replied, a little breathlessly.

'May I see your Pay Book, please,' asked one, who I could now see was a sergeant.

'Sure,' I replied, taking out my AB 64 Part I and handing it over.

'What's your number?'

'14162034,' I replied, instantly.

'What's your hurry, soldier, it's not that late?' asked the sergeant.

'No,' I said, sheepishly. 'I dunno, really. I've just met a new girl, and she agreed to come to the pictures with me tomorrow,' I explained, lamely.

The other policeman chuckled. 'Right oh, son. Just watch it. Mind you don't do anything naughty. Dangerous things, women, an' you'll have as much trouble as you can handle, before very long, I dare say. Mind she don't blame you for something you haven't done – that's if you haven't done it.'

They both laughed. The sergeant handed over my Pay Book.

'Good-night, son,' said the constable.

'Good-night,' I replied.

I had calmed down now, and I made the rest of the journey at a more sedate pace.

I signed in at the gate. I looked down the list for Bill's signature. Bill was still out. Things must be progressing with Josie. The sergeant of the guard was resting, and the corporal was on duty.

'Well, look 'oo it is.' The amused corporal was Foot, with a PTW guard. 'Look at this, then, he went on, addressing the sentry waiting to go on duty at 2000 hours; 'this is Private Milton, of my last intake. Nice lad, 'e was, when I was looking after 'im. Good at chucking grenades, too. Look at 'im, now! Private Milton, you've got lipstick all over your physog, and powder, in heaps on your collar. You look like a tit in a trance. Private Jones, just check that his button are done up – *ALL* his buttons! Smarten yourself up, lad; you've joined this lot ter fight Jerry, not ter get up 'arf the birds that 'ang ararnd *The Jolly Boatmen*.'

By the time Bill crept in, I was fast asleep.

The next day was a routine one. PT and drill were followed by a health talk where the dangers and horrors of VD were outlined, in very graphic terms, by a medical officer. The action to be taken by any soldier who thought that he had exposed himself to such a risk, was explained to us. There was a little treatment room alongside the guard room of most of the larger camps known as the PAC centre (personal action against contamination). Any man so inclined could go and carry out a simple personal cleansing process as soon as he returned to camp. This would at least give him peace of mind!

After this, we had a longer than usual break. This was because the instructors were siting some 'snipers' – carefully camouflaged – who were being set out, as an object lesson and an observation test for the platoon. During this period Bill came across to where I was sitting on a patch of grass.

'Ow' d'yer make out then,' he asked, as an opening gambit.

'OK,' I replied, 'we're going ter the Odeon, tonight.' There was a moment of silence. 'She's nice,' I went on, lamely.

'Where yer meetin' 'er?' Bill went on.

'I'm calling round 'er place,' I admitted.

'Cor, Blimey! Meetin' the folks, already, eh! You are getting yer feet under the table, aren't yer? Cor, I'd never 'ave thought it of you, George, straight I wouldn't.'

''Ow d'you make out with Josie, then?' I asked, anxious to change the subject.

'Very nice. Josie's awlright. Needs a bit of chatting up of course – she's a bit choosey. Not like some o' the tarts round the arcade – only do it fer friends and strangers!'

'Cor, 'ark at 'im. If she's choosey, mate, 'ow come she'll talk ter you?' The speaker was Jim Dodson.

'You wouldn't understand, young Dodson. I know the sort you go sniffing around – saw yer last week, talking ter that skinny bird by the clock tower. When you squeezed 'er 'and, she said, "I don't, usually, but you've talked me into it".' Bill looked round with a smirk, while the others had a good laugh.

Jim Dodson laughed. 'You're a bloody liar, Bill Smith,' he said, without malice. 'Mine won't drop off through putting it in the wrong place, mate.'

'I 'ope you gave it the old copper penny test,' went on Bill.

'No need fer anything like that. She's a nice girl, an she knows a good bloke, when she sees one.'

This last remark brought some derisive laughter from the squaddies. The conversation was interrupted by the arrival of the platoon sergeant, Sergeant Dent.

'Right, get fell in, you men,' he said, crisply.

We assembled, and were marched out to the edge of the camp, where we followed a country lane for some way. We left-wheeled down a farm track, and were halted. Here we met the company commander, Captain Buck, and the platoon commander, Lieutenant Spry.

We made our way, in twos and threes. In front of us, the landscape fell away as scrub land, with grass, bushes, and the odd tree.

'Sit down, men, along this ridge,' ordered the platoon commander. Captain Buck stood to one side, a pair of binoculars round his neck.

Lieutenant Spry took over. 'Now, men, look to your front. Out there are six men, who've got you in their sights. Quarter the ground carefully, and see how many you can spot. The first one is very close.'

We covered the ground methodiocally with our eyes, as we had been taught. I was next to Jim Dodson, and next to him was Paddy Logan.

'Can you see anybody, Jim?' asked Paddy.

'Sod all,' said Jim. 'Wait a minute, though; I can just see a ladybird, ten o'clock, two hundred yards. Only thing is, I can't see 'ow many spots it's got.'

'Has anybody found them, yet?' asked the officer. Nobody had.

'Right; watch, carefully; half right, one hundred yards.' He blew a short blast on a whistle.

'I think I saw a movement, sir,' called a private on the right hand end.

'Where?'

'Just there, sir.'

'Come on, private; give the correct designation,' said Lieutenant Spry.

'Two o'clock, sir; one hundred yards. Small green shrub, sir.' Then the lieutenant gave two long blasts on his whistle. It was then that the 'green bush' rose into the air, and was seen as a sniper, heavily camouflaged.

'Look to your front,' went on the platoon commander. He then gave one short blast. To everyone's amazement, a figure seemed to rise out of the earth. It reminded me of the fighting men rising up from the sowing of the dragon's teeth. He was a mere thirty yards in front of us, and he had been lying in the open. More surprises were to follow. On successive blasts of the whistle, four other figures rose up. All were cleverly camouflaged. what surprised me most was that all of them were in the open – they had not been hiding behind trees or rocks.

After dinner, we spent the afternoon on more camouflage exercises. We were shown how to darken our hands and faces, using whatever was to hand – be it blanco, cocoa, mud, or even cow dung! We all practised personal camouflage. One section went to ground, and the other two sections had to try to spot them. The sections took it in turn to try to hide. We were not allowed to take cover behind any obstacle. Paddy was quickly spotted. When one of his 'oppos' let out a squeaky fart, he moved his head to look at the offender. The slight movement gave him away. Sergeant Dent was not amused.

I had to hurry. Cleaning off the camouflage took time, and my face hand hands were quite sore from desperate scrubbing. My careful preparations did not pass, unnoticed.

'Make sure yer've got everything, just in case it's yer lucky night.'

'If 'er mum gets in the way, promise ter give 'er a tumble next!'

''Ow about some of this, then,' called out another hard-boiled hut mate. I was carefully arranging my hair, but I was ill-advised enough to look round at the grinning figure holding his fore arm upright with fist clenched.

'You're a lot of filthy-minded buggers,' I laughed, as I made my final preparations.

I made my way through the High Street, down Station Road, and along the cobbled alley. As I approached the house again, I noticed a tightening in the pit of the stomach. I rang the bell.

'Answer the door, Mum,' called a voice, from upstairs.

Nothing loth, Stella's mother was already pattering down the little hall.

'Hallo, you must be George. Come in. Stella's still getting changed.' She led me into the sitting room.

'Sit down, George.' Mrs, Hughes – that was Stella's surname – was a cherubic-looking lady in her early forties. She seemed slightly reassured by what she saw. One could not be too careful in a town like this, full of all sorts, coming and going. The boys from up at that camp could be a tough lot, especially the lads from the London area. I seemed to pass muster on first acquaintance. Also, I believe, she had considerable faith in Stella's judgement, and I had been given a 'clean bill of health'. I could understand her concern – there were some very rough boys at the camp! She asked me the usual questions – where I came from, my family, my job, and so on. I answered all her questions, without demur. As I said, I knew what was behind it all, and I didn't mind.

After ten minutes, Stella came down. She had changed into a neat, attractive two-piece suit, ideal for the Cheshire winter. She wore a white blouse, buttoned at the neck. She looked very pretty. I certainly thought so, as I rose from the armchair into which Mrs Hughes had thrust me.

'Hallo,' she said, with a smile.

'Hallo,' I said back, not knowing quite what to do or say.

'We'll be off, then, Mum,' she said. 'Don't suppose we'll be too late back.'

She took me possessively by the arm as we walked down the road. There was no need to go back through the High Street as we were able to cut along the back roads, and come out at the corner where the cinema was.

I tried to pay for both tickets, but Stella slipped some money into my pocket. We were lucky. As we were ushered to two seats at the back of the stalls, the Gaumount British News reel was just showing. We watched the news reel. The war news was mainly from North Africa, with hoards of prisoners, tanks churning up the sand, and bare-kneed, tin-hatted infantry, moving forward.

By the time that the news reel had ended and the trailers of next week's programme were being shown, I had managed to find Stella's left hand, which was resting on her lap. The contact sent a small thrill up my arm, and I sat still while she rested her hand in mine – her small, dainty hand, in my weathered, muscular paw!

We became engrossed in the Bob Hope comedy. Stella laughed hilariously, and leant close to me. After screwing up my courage to the sticking place, and following several false starts, I finally passed my left arm round her shoulders. This manoeuvre appeared to be welcome, because she snuggled closer to me. We were strategically placed, in the centre of the back row of stalls. I felt possessive and possessed – a new experience – as we cuddled closer. Stella still seemed to be following the rather shallow plot of the film, but I had rather lost the thread. I was breaking new ground, and I was gearing myself up for the next step. Emboldened by my initial progress, and forcing myself to break out of my shell of shyness and inexperience, I brought my right hand up, with infinite caution, and rested it inside her coat. She kept very still. With daring born of desperation, I moved the tips of my fingers and came into contact with one of the little, rounded buttons of her blouse. One of the buttons came undone – the button-hole must have been worn. She still kept motionless – almost tense. As though mesmerised, I gently nudged the next button undone, and eased my hand inside. I felt her catch her breath as my hand contracted, gently, over the cup of her bra. She still appeared to be concentrating on the film. For minutes, I kept my hand quite still while she became accustomed to its presence.

What next? Dare I! As my probing fingers moved, I found that the elastic centre of the bra stretched easily, and I was able to expose her left breast. Almost before I was aware of what was happening, I was touching her. I could feel the firming nipple, and I caressed it, very gently. Without undue haste, and equally gently, she removed my hand, adjusted her bra and blouse, and held my hand firmly in her lap. She did not seem to have minded, and I did not feel as though I had been chastened or rebuked. She still clung close, and kissed my ear lightly.

There was little further incident. On reflection, I was a bit taken aback by my own boldness, and apparent success. At the end of the programme, we picked our way out into the lighted foyer. Stella quickly disappeared. I smiled to myself. I remembered a previous similar occasion, when I had waited for Joyce at the end of the dance. I didn't think that I need have any fear that this one would run out on me.

It was cold outside. She shivered slightly, giving me the excuse I wanted.

'It's still early. Would you like to go for a cup of coffee, or something?' I asked.

She thought about it. 'No,' she replied, after some thought; 'I've got a better plan. We could go back, and you could come in for a while.'

'You mean, back to your home?' I asked.

'Yes. We could make a drink or something, before you go back,' she suggested.

Wondering where all this would lead me, I escorted her home the way we had come. The back streets were much quieter than the crowded, main streets of the city. It was very dark in places, and I felt confident enough to draw her to one side, and kiss her. Her nose was cold, but her lips were warm and generous. Without seeming to hurry me, she drew away, took my arm, and persuaded me to continue the journey.

I waited behind her as she opened the door with a key.

'Mum has gone round to Auntie May's – that's Pete's mum, to play cards.'

I had been meaning to ask about Stella's father, but thought better of it. He certainly didn't seem to be in evidence, and now I suddenly found myself in a situation that normally came only in dreams. Mum, it seemed, played whist regularly on Thursdays, and would probably get back quite late. They would meet in *The Crown;* Mrs. Hughes, Mrs. Drage, and two other ladies. After a gin or two, they would go back and play cards until about mid-night. Mrs. Drage lived quite near, and so it was no trouble to walk home afterwards. I could find out nothing about any husbands.

Christ, what would my mates say, if they knew! I could hear Bill Smith, with his 'Got yer feet under the table, then!' What would Paddy say? Probably, 'Get in Nob, it's yer birfday!' No doubt there would be some expressions of envy, and they would expect a blow by blow account.

Stella took her coat off. She put on the gas fire in the sitting room, and joned me on the settee. Nothing was said about making a drink. With the lights out, the only glow came from the low-set gas fire. She had taken her outdoor shoes off, and wore fluffy slippers. She unbuttoned my heavy, wool BD tunic, and I took it off. I felt ludicrous, with my Army braces exposed, and I wondered what she expected me to do. I had little idea, and I felt that I should have to proceed very cautiously, and hope for her to take some of the initiative. She looked at me challengingly – or teasingly. I put my arm round her shoulders and kissed her, firmly and passionately, pressing her down into the corner of the settee.

She looked at me shrewdly. 'You are learning fast, aren't you? I think you're a bit of a dark horse.'

I grinned wryly. She had drawn her feet up on to the settee, losing her slippers in the process. We clinched, in a long, restless kiss, clutching tightly at each other. Without more ado, I undid the same, unreliable blouse button, and confronted her bra. 'God,' I wondered, 'how do you get round this?'

While I fumbled, she said softly, 'It unhooks, at the back.' She raised herself, very slightly, and I found the hook.

Well, I had already done better than I had with that ejection opening cover on the bren gun! Perhaps the sergeant would be proud of me! Now, with the released garment moved up out of the way, I felt the neat, firm whiteness of her breasts. Her eyes had been half-closed, but she opened them wide and looked up at me, with a sort of innocence and trust; trust to do what? After another, passionate interlude, I felt my right hand moving down inexorably, past her waist, to her hip. Still the hand descended, as though under hypnosis, until I could feel the hem of her skirt, and the vertical thread of stocking, on the inside of her thigh.

I felt a pounding in my ears, and my throat was dry. Then her hand was on mine, pulling me away, gently but firmly. Oddly, I had a strange feeling of relief – an awareness that I might be getting out of my depth – and she looked at me as I leaned over, and shook her head slowly from side to side. She was smiling perhaps wistfully.

'You are rather sweet,' she said, and kissed me. 'Time's getting on; I'll make some tea.'

I looked at my watch in absolute amazement. Perhaps I had not been such a fast worker after all! She sat up, and adjusted her bra and buttons.

'You'll have that button off,' she said, ruefully.

She brushed her hair and went into the kitchen, while I found my way to the bathroom. This time, the pain in the pit of the stomach had been replaced by a pain lower down, where my recent excitement and degree of expectancy was causing problems.

This time, when I went back to camp, I didn't run. I had left ample time, and my mind was crowded with kaleidoscopic flashes of thought.

I thought, with some awe, of the events of the evening, from the intimate caress in the dark cinema, to the unveiling on the settee. What would she have done, if I had continued, boldly, and without mercy, to undress her? Her skirt, I had noticed, was supported by elastic in the waist, and buttons at the side. How hard would she have tried to stop me if I had tried to take her, there and then?

I walked out of the city, along the more open road leading back to camp. Suppose she had just been playing 'hard to get', and had been expecting my wandering hands to have carried on and remove the other essentials. Was she disappointed at me? Had she allowed any other feller to do what I didn't do, on the settee? Perhaps I had been a fool. Perhaps I should carry a packet of Durex, as I had been advised to do by my wiser mates. I had heard that some girls were more willing if the boy was thus prepared.

Of course, I had to report progress to the others. This was awkward, because Stella was, after all, the cousin of one of the boys down the lines. I should have liked to embellish the tale – to have given an exciting account. As it was, I confided in Bill who, although rough and tough, could be trusted not to let a mate down, either over a confidence, or in a rough house.

We were meeting on Saturday, in the afternoon. I was going round to tea. In the evening, we were going to meet some of the others, in *The Jolly Boatmen*.

On Friday afternoon, the blow fell.

The Part III order was terse and explicit.

'The undermentioned O/Rs' were to be posted to the 70th Battalion, in Hounslow, West London, the following Wednesday. My name was there; so were the names of Geoff Collard, John Lewin and Jim Dodson. Paddy, Bill Smith, and about half of hut 12, were staying – waiting to be posted to service battalions. Those posted to the 70th were the younger ones who had joined up. It was the, largely older, conscripts, who were staying. The younger ones were not yet quite of an age where they could be sent overseas.

Of course, I had known that I would not stay up here so much longer, but the news was still a shock. For the first time, the significance of leaving wives or sweethearts behind became apparent. What was I to do? What would Stella say when I told her?

There was a lot to be done. The Saturday afternoon tea was off! I would be in my hut, sorting out my kit prior to a thorough inspection at 1600 hours. On Monday we were to parade for an FFI (medical inspection), and we would be off early on Wednesday, after having checked in our rifles and taken our palliasses out for emptying.

When I called round to see Stella, at 6 o'clock on Saturday, it was obvious that she knew. She smiled and appeared composed, but she was pale. I stayed for a while, talking to Mrs. Hughes.

'Well, you'll be near home, George.' she said, 'You'll be able to visit your mother quite often.'

Stella said little. She took my arm as we went later to meet the others. There was an unpleasant drizzle, and we hurried along. I was not wearing my greatcoat, and I leaned forward into the rain. We soon arrived, and we were welcomed by mates already there. The soldiers talked about the postings, and the girls listened. Postings were a fact of life – here today, and gone tomorrow.

The evening wore on. Stella remained comparatively quiet, and I tried to cheer her up with a light banter, that came mighty hard to me just then. I could see that her eyes were watery, and the sight provoked mixed feelings. Here was another newish experience; someone was crying about me! True, my mother had wept, silently and unashamedly, the day I joined up. It all seemed a long time ago, as I sat in this pub, trying to consol my first girl friend to the fact that I was going. The fact that someone could be that bothered about me was still a novelty.

We left early, before the others. She took my arm as we walked home. I went inside. Mrs. Hughes was about – it wasn't Thursday – but she busied herself cooking, and she left the sitting room to us.

'What are you going to do, George?' asked Stella, in a small voice.

What was I going to do! Paddy Logan and Bill Smith had already given me their considered opinion.

69

'Give 'er the soldier's farewell, Tosh. You 'ave ter tell 'er you luv 'er, an' all that stuff. Tell 'er that you'll come back ter see 'er. You won't 'ave any trouble, mate. She's fallen for yer, an' she'll be expectin' it now. Be careful though. Don't go putting 'er in the club. She'll find someone else, arter you've gone.'

Of course, mine wasn't the only liaison that had to be broken. There were a number of others who had got their feet under the table, but they were all young, and those concerned, of both sexes, would soon recover.

'How much do you like me, George?' she asked, softly.

This was my cue, of course. I had only to say the right things, and, time and place provided, she would be mine!

'I think a lot of you,' I said, awkwardly, 'you know that.'

'I like you a lot, too, darling,' she replied. She broke into a fit of little sobs, and, throwing her arms round me, kissed me with an abandon that left me trembling. I felt an almost overwhelming urge to pursue my advantage and to hell with the consequences. Had it been Thursday night, instead of Saturday, I might have acted on the camp advice. I drew away, my mind in a confused whirl. What did I feel for her?

'I think I love you,' she said, suddenly and humbly.

Now I was really embarrassed, but I spoke quietly.

'Stella – darling – you don't know anything about me. You've only known me a few days.'

'That's long enough to know – a girl can tell. Will you come back, sometimes?' she asked.

'I don't know, Stella – I like you a lot; but we know so little about each other. I'll write to you – honest I will, and I'll come and see you, when I can,' I promised.

She wept, bitterly. I felt a bit like crying myself. Mrs. Hughes came in, with three cups on a tray, and some pastries she had made. Stella dried her eyes, and we drank our tea. She had calmed down. Mrs. Hughes did her best, but she felt a bit helpless. Poor Stella. This was the first time that she had been really 'bitten'. Still, he was a nice lad, with a good family background, and a job to go back to. She realised, of course, that anything could happen in the next few years. Also, she realised, the current occupation of soldiering wasn't exactly a safe one. She also realised that had I been around for a few more months, anything might have happened. As it was, she accepted that I was on my way, like all soldiers. Stella would get over it, and we were both very young. If we kept in touch and I came back, Mrs. Hughes would be happy to accept the situation.

I still had my mates to put up with back at camp. To them, she was a girl who had become vulnerable – whose defences had been breached – and, as far as they were concerned, I should press home my attack and effect a conquest – very nice, too! They wanted to know the gory details. Had it been alright. Had she been very difficult? Was I the first? Had I had to promise to marry her before she would give in?

I was feeling thoroughly miserable, but I did my best to keep my temper. They meant no harm.

Bill was trumps. He was a shrewd lad, and he sensed the deeper, albeit temporary, agonies.

After Sunday church parade, we went for a stroll around the camp, and we ended up in the NAAFI. It was almost empty, having just opened. Most of the squaddies were back in their billet, reading the papers, or getting ready to go out later.

'Hallo, darling,' chirped Bill, on seeing Sue at the counter. ''Ow d'yer date go, then?'

She gave a wry grimace. 'Oh, alright. They were quite nice fellers. We went for a dance, and had a drink.' She glanced at me coyly, and, I thought, a little embarrased.

'Me mate's posted,' said Bill.

'Oh?' She looked at me, in dismay.

'Yes,' I said, breezily, 'I'm off to London, Wednesday.'

'Bit sudden, isn't it?' she said.

'No, not really, I suppose,' I replied. 'I knew it was bound to happen, soon.'

I took Stella out in the afternoon. I did not have to call for her, as she was meeting me by the clock tower. It was a crisp, sunny day, quite pleasant, and surprisingly mild for late November. We walked round the park and by the river. She was quite composed now. We walked, hand in hand, slowly and lazily. There was a change – a slight change, but she did seem a little more distant. Subconsciously perhaps, she had accepted that I was to go. Deep down, I suppose she thought that the chances of my rushing back to see her at every opportunity, were very small. Anyway, opportunities would be limited. there was little for her to pin any hope on. There had not been quite enough time, she thought, and so it would be a case of 'what might have been'.

I stayed for tea, and we sat around, holding hands. I had not the heart to start anything tonight. I had, in fact, been touched, almost shaken, by her attachment to me, and this very devotion had defeated me. I was not tough enough to try to blackmail her into a submission, although I realised this might well have worked.

I left quite early. On the way back, I met some platoon mates and joined them for a boozy sing song. Several of them had sorrows to drown, and drunken renderings of the songs of the day helped to bring our melancholia to the surface, where it could be washed away in a stream of beer. *The Bells are Ringing* was sung with great emotion, as the besotted squaddies raised their voices, pint glasses in hand, and arms around each other's shoulders. The journey back to camp was, to say the least, erratic. Our staggering progress was punctuated with stops by convenient trees or brick walls. Not without difficulty, the least drunk among us were able to straighten up our mates sufficiently to negotiate the guard room. I was the worse for wear, and I was being urged into a presentable state by John Lewin, who, having no unfinished affair to cope with, was fairly sober.

'Brace up, George, for Christ's sake!' he said, shaking me by the shoulder as we approached the gate. 'Do your bloody collar up, and get yer bloody hat on. Sergeant Best's on guard, an' he can be a right bastard.'

'He can get stuffed,' I mumbled. 'He can please his bloody self, if he wants to put me inside.'

'Shut up, you silly bugger!' said someone. They got me fairly presentable and steered me into the guard room, where John signed me in. The corporal on duty looked at them meaningly as they strove to keep me upright.

'Get that noisy bastard off to bed before the sergeant hears him,' he said.

We made it. I slept in a drunken stupor. I woke once, and was forced to go outside. Morning found me with a grey face and a bad head, but passable. Fortunately, it was a day of lectures and tactical exercises, and I got through.

There is little more to tell. Stella had pleaded with her boss, that her boy friend was leaving. She begged a little time to see me off at the station at 9 o'clock on Wednesday morning. Her boss readily agreed. He knew that he would get no work out of her until the draft had gone.

There were other girls there, too.

We arrived, by truck, and made for the reserved carriages, staggering under FMO, and lugging loaded kit bags.

She kissed me, and wiped away a few tears.

'Write when you can, George,' she said, quietly.

'OK. Cheerio, darling,' I said.

We were gone.

Chapter Six

The 70th Battalion was different.

To start with, the soldiers were young, eighteen or nineteen. To most of us, it meant a move nearer home. The barracks, west of Hounslow, gave access to a London, where many of them came from. Most of the others were also from the South, and the change of scene was welcome.

In some ways, the move was tough. Perhaps this was partly due to the fact that the regiment was on home ground, and had to prove something; or perhaps it was to crush any sign of incipient slackness among these often aggressive youngsters, most of whom had joined for action.

The training staff set exacting standards, and the permanent maintenance staff were most of them old sweats.

The camp was a large one, mainly brick huts, with roads and side roads. It had been built alongside the old cavalry barracks, which was now used mainly for administration. It also housed the regimental band of the Royal Fusiliers.

The draft marched through the gate, thankful to have arrived, whatever the future held. We had come out from London on a suburban train, and we had marched through the town to the camp, situated on the outskirts.

My shoulders ached from my large pack, small pack and kit bag. Like the others, I carried my kit bag slung over my left shoulder, with some of the weight resting on the packs. My hands were stained with blanco from my equipment, and my mouth was dry. To exist on haversack rations, you had to have the digestive system of a goat. These rations had been collected after breakfast. They were kept in one's mess tins, in the small pack. They were two metal tins, and one fitted inside the other. The system was to put the food in the smaller one, to prevent it drying out. The sandwiches were usually uncut slices of bread, thinly spread with margarine. The sandwich filling could be spam, paste (fish or meat), jam (plum or gooseberry), and occasionally cheese. Haversack rations were for the hungry! All of this was washed down with warm water, from a metal water carrier that one had carried around all day. The water bottle had a screw-in metal 'cork' attached to a piece of thin cord. The water carrier fitted into the small pack, alongside the mess tins. A small pack also carried a spare pair of socks and a holdall, containing knife, fork, spoon, razor, comb and lather brush, in that order.

Hut 16 was in 'B' company lines, and housed Number 1 platoon. It was brick, like all the others. There was a brick-edged concrete path, leading to the narrow door. All the bricks edging the path were at an angle of forty-five degrees, and all were red – a carefully polished red! Around the door there was a pattern of polished bricks. The mortar was picked out in white paint. The floor of the hut was covered in brown lino. There was the usual stove, very black and shiny. Near the stove, was a coal bucket. It was very highly polished, so that the outside reflected, like a mirror. It was not used for coal!

The bunks were smaller than those in Hut 12, but in better condition. Mattresses were straw palliasses.

We new arrivals were distributed among the platoons, to bring them back up to strength. We were replacing those who had been drafted to battalions. The previous tenants were on their way to units – somewhere in the Middle East.

There was the usual scramble for the best sited beds. This time, I got a bottom bunk, along the middle of one side of the hut. This meant that I was near the stove. There was the usual trestle table and two trestle benches. The table was very clean, as were the benches.

We went through the usual routine of filling palliasses and collecting blankets. Then we stripped off and took soap and towels to the ablutions near by. The water was cold, and wash basin stoppers were scarce. The basins were very clean.

Jim Dodson had been assigned to 'A' company. John Lewin was in 'B' company, number 2 platoon, with Geoff Collard.

The newcomers paraded at 1900 hours. Our Pay Books were taken in, for making up, and our numbers and names were checked off from a nominal roll. We were ushered into a lecture hut. After the documentation was complete, a burly figure entered. RSM Jones! He was of medium height, upright, impeccably turned out, and he had medal ribbons on his tunic. The story was that he had got his MM for using a shovel against the enemy, with terrible effect! This time, fortunately, he was carrying a pacing stick and not a shovel. My sympathies were, instinctively, with the enemy.

His voice was harsh – like the voices of most soldiers who had given countless orders on the square – and he had a gold-capped tooth that was visible when he shouted an order.

'Right men, if you don't know who I am, you soon will!' was his opening gambit. He looked around at the young strained, but attentive faces. 'This is a smart unit, in a smart camp, an' we turn out smart soldiers. You will always be smart and correctly dressed, when you go out of camp. You will, always move about briskly when you are in camp. If you let down the battalion outside, you will be INSIDE so fast yer feet won't touch the ground. You are going ter be soldiers – first-class, ready ter fight, ready fer anything, infantry! I don't want ter hear of youse fellers doin' all yer fight'n down town, an' I don't want anybody's blooming, like a big, red rose! Be careful which girls you knock about with. We got the usual treatment centre, by the guard room. If you have any doubts, go sick.' He glared around the squad, and then continued: 'Best thing is – leave the town tarts alone – you're 'ere to fight 'Itler, not go chasing bits of skirt all over London. Oh, yes, I almost forgot – you will get yer 'air cut on Friday – every Friday!'

He left. One of the platoon sergeants took over, and paraded us to collect rifles and have the numbers booked. Then we were ordered back to our billets to clean the rifles ready for the morning inspection. We each collected a set of denims at the same time, and went off feeling rather chastened. There was just time to inspect the NAAFI and get some supper there. It was very similar to the previous one – the usual piano was there, as well as the standard issue tables and chairs. It didn't look too inviting.

The rest of number 2 platoon had arrived a few weeks earlier. They were all young soldiers, of course.

When I got back from the NAAFI, I wrote to Stella. I was feeling lonely and miserable – having had a few roots torn in the transplanting. I poured out some of my troubles, on paper; told her how much I missed her, and how I wished I could be with her. Having posted my letter, I felt a bit happier. It was now, hopefully, on its way to Cheshire.

The morning was bright and clear. We washed and shaved. The water was just warm. Then we straightened up the room. Room inspections were very strict. I was told that every Saturday morning there was a hut competition, and that this was a serious business; the company commander came and his inspections were very thorough. Rivalry was keen.

The training was arduous, as was to be expected, and we were back to infantry weapon training and infantry tactics. The MMG's were, temporarily at least, a thing of the past.

After the rifle inspection, the platoon was drilled on the square. The rifle inspection had gone off, O.K., except that one luckless private had a grubby barrel, and he was promptly 'put on a charge', on the instructions of the platoon officer, Lieutenant Watkins.

'This man's rifle is filthy, sergeant – put him on a charge,' was all he had said. The luckless soldier's name and number were booked by the sergeant, who would now have to write out the charge, on a form, 252, and present it to the CSM. On the following day, or Monday for Friday charges, he would parade at the company office, smartly dressed. He would be inspected by the CSM, who would march him in to the company commander for summary justice. The usual sentence was a stretch of C.B. (confined to barracks).

However, as will be seen later, it involved much more than just being kept in.

The drill was not too bad. It didn't take long for the new men to blend in with the others. The huge square echoed to the sound of barked commands, as various platoons were being put through their paces.

There was a welcome change to the routine that afternoon. The platoon was paraded, and marched to the Education Centre. Here, we were 'fell out', and the corporal, who had escorted us, retired, leaving us to the mercy of a studious looking sergeant. The sergeant wore the shoulder flashes of the Army Education Corps, with the appropriate blue bar on his sleeve. This was my first experience of ABCA, and I found it a very pleasant change from the normal routine.

The Army prided itself that it kept its troops informed about the goings on in the world, even in war time, and they set up a Bureau of Current Affairs to produce a series of potted lectures on general subjects (less sex, religion and politics). They issued notes to the AEC, and then the education sergeant tried to conduct discussions, based on the guide lines. Today, the topic was the cause of the war and a short history of Poland. A few of the lads were mildly interested, but most of them regarded it as a welcome rest in a hut, sitting in a chair instead of spending a cold afternoon on battle drill.

I found myself enjoying the afternoon. I joined in the discussion with animation, so that it became virtually a dialogue between me and the instructor. When we had finished the new men were interviewed by the NCO while the others were given an opportunity to read books and pamphlets.

'Well, who're you, then?' The sergeant came and sat in a chair by me. He had a note book.

'034, Private Milton, sergeant,' I replied, automatically.

'You just arrived from the MGTC?' he asked.

'Yes, sergeant,' I replied.

'You've had quite a bit to say this afternoon,' he went on. 'What were you doing, before you joined up?'

He built up the story of my background and quizzed me about my plan for the future.

'Are you going to apply to be a candidate for commission?' he asked.

'No, sergeant,' I replied. 'Well, I don't really know what I shall do – whether I shall apply, or just stay in the ranks.'

'Will you get your old job back?'

'Yes, very likely,' I replied. I went on to explain about my job, and the studies that I had undertaken just prior to joining up.

'There's an advanced science evening course running at the polytechnic, just down the road,' said the sergeant. 'There's no reason why you shouldn't go along. I could get you enrolled – the Army pays the fees.'

I was interested. It would certainly be a change to go along and brush up on the maths and chemistry. 'Yes, I'd rather like that, if it could be arranged, sergeant,' I said.

The other good thing about the education afternoon was that it finished in good time, and, if we were lucky, and had no more duties, we could go out.

I decided to take this opportunity to give the town the once over. I was already wearing BD, because of the education parade. It was nearly a mile to the centre, but I decided against taking a bus because I wanted to get my bearings. I negotiated the guard room and walked down the residential street, past the cavalry barracks, to the main road into Hounslow. I noticed the 'semis', on either side of the street. Living in them were civilians, leading lives of daily routine, going to work or school, largely unaware of the gulf between their world and that of the men who daily passed by the gate. Their lives were their own; there was no-one to chase them around, or put them on a charge for having a button undone. They had their own private lives. They were not regimented, numbered and thrust into heartless, soulless military camps.

I was feeling fed up with the Army, and very lonely. I had just found someone who thought me desirable, and now she was gone – hundreds of miles away. How I wished I was back in Chester, with Bill Smith and my other old mates. The thought of Stella made me so unhappy, I thought of running away. What was she doing now? What would she be doing tonight? She hadn't written, and I was in a state of despair. I longed for civilian company – contact with people from the other world, that was so near, but from which I was so firmly divorced.

I walked on, passing pubs and shops, and making mental notes. On the right was the entrance to the Underground, and opposite was a row of shops. As I came into the town proper, I found several more pubs and another Underground station. It was early December, and the shops were becoming Christmassy, in a subdued, rationed way.

I wandered about, being careful not to put my hands in my pockets and keeping a weather eye open for officers. I found the bus depot, from which I would be able to get a bus to take me quite close to home. There was a pleasant looking Italian café near the edge of town. I ordered a coffee and a bun, and looked around. People were scurrying past the window, going home from work or from shopping. Bicycles and cars went by, their headlights masked to conform with regulations. Perhaps at the weekend, I would have a chance to go home for the day and lick my emotional wounds. If only circumstances had worked out differently, and Stella had lived here in Hounslow! The idea of going home was not so exciting after all. There was no Stella there. The day would be empty with neighbours asking questions and parents looking at me, as though I might vanish in a puff of smoke.

I sat with another cup of coffee and watched the world go by. My loneliness washed over me. I went out to investigate the rest of the town. I was just getting used to the idea that I was now so close to home – close to shops and streets that were familior to me. In some ways it was unsettling – I was so close to home, and yet already, after a few weeks, I was separated from my previous life by a chasm of commitment and new experiences.

I looked in at *The Lion*. It was in the main street and was showing early signs of life. The evening was still young. I bought a half and sat at one of the small round tables. One or two couples came in, laughing and sharing little private conversations. Again, I felt a wave of self-pity – an unutterable jealousy of these happy couples. One particular pair caught by eye. The man was a smooth, confident civvy, in his early twenties. 'Ought to be in the bloody Kate,' I thought, uncharitably. She was dark, with saucy eyes, seemingly reflecting an inner knowledge of what it was all about. She had a vivaceous smile. As Bill would have said, 'She knows 'ow many bloody beans make five!' I surveyed her analytically. I wondered if her bra unhooked, at the back as well. Would she shake her head, and put out a firm, restraining hand when her escort's groping fingers got to work? I thought it unlikely, and I formed an illogical hatred for her escort. The smooth bastard would be there! He had probably been there already. No doubt, he had passed through the barrier of carnal experience, and so possessed a wisdom of infinite depth, compared with mine.

An older couple came in. They were obviously spliced. She'd be going to bed with the old man tonight, and make it all available, with no head shaking or hassle. I got to wondering about the married state – of getting into bed with a woman ready and willing – night after night.

'Hello, Tosh. What makes you look so bloody miserable, then? Has she buggered off with another bloke?'

I came to with a start. The speaker was a lean, muscular soldier from the regiment. With him was Jim Dodson.

'Hello, George, me old mate,' said Jim; 'Meet me pal, 'er, Charlie – Charlie Brown. Charlie, this is George, an' an old pal from Chester. 'E's new, too, an' looks bloody fed up. Oh, o' course, I was fergetting. Sorry, George. I forgot you left a bit of lumber back up North.' They both laughed.

'Cheer up, me ol' son,' said Charlie. 'Let me get you annuvver one, before you bust out crying. She's probably fergotten yer by now, anyway – stuck up against the wall by a bloody Yank, shouldn't wonder.'

I felt a hot denial rising in my throat. What was the use!

Charlie brought the drinks over, and we all sat round the little table. Quite a few more soldiers were coming in now, and the place had livened up.

The company had certainly helped.

"Erd anyfing from yer bird yet, George?' asked Jim.

'No,' I replied, shortly.

'S'pose you've written? Yeah, course you have,' he said, looking at my face.

'Yeah, I wrote a couple a days ago,' I replied.

'Well; blimey – she can't write back, till she knows yer bleedin' address, yer daft sod!' chortled Jim.

What a fool I was! Of course she would write. She had to wait for my letter before she knew my address. I felt as though a weight had been lifted off my shoulders. I looked at Jim with gratitude.

'Come on; drink up, you two buggers.' I said; 'My turn ter get one in.'

Next morning, sure enough, there was a letter from Stella. I wouldn't have recognised the backward-sloping writing, but the Chester postmark was clear. My heart sang as I sat on my bunk and read it. It was quite a long letter, full of endearments. There was some news, too. Paddy Logan and Bill Smith had been sent on embarkation leave. They were going to the 1st battalion. This was an open secret. The 1st battalion was in the Middle East.

I read the letter several times during the day, trying to read in some message or innuendo that I had missed.

The following day was to be a hard one. We collected haversack rations and paraded in the roadway, in FSMO, with rifles and carrying bren gun magazines in our pouches.

We were stretched to the limit, that day. After a forced march across the heath, we came to some open countryside, pock-marked with gravel workings, many of them flooded. We were rested, in a hollow, while the 'O' group conferred. The Army system of communication, from OC to private, was verbal, by briefings. Thus, the 'O' group was briefed by the company commander, Major Smythe. 'O' group included platoon officers and sergeants. The platoon officers then briefed the section commanders, and they briefed the men. Each platoon consisted of three sections, of about nine men. Each section was divided into rifle group and bren group. There was often a lance corporal in charge of the bren group. The basic principle of infantry battle drill was the mutual support of group by group, so that you advanced while being supported by your comrades. Cover was often given by smoke, which could be provided by grenade or by mortar bomb.

Anyway, our section made the most of the rest, while the 'brass' conferred. Simply, the company was going to capture a wooden hillock some mile or so away.

Number 1 platoon hooked themselves together, and slung their rifles over their shoulders and hooked their chin straps under their chins. We proceeded along a sunken, hedge-lined lane, which approached the target obliquely, to the right. The sections moved in single file, well apart, in staggered formation along the sides of the road. Infantry usually advanced this way to their starting point. They were trained not to bunch, in case of strafing from the air.

The riflemen were issued with blank rounds, and the NCOs were nursing thunder flashes and bakelite grenades. These grenades made a lot of noise, but were considered fairly harmless; that is, as long as you didn't get hit by the flying firing mechanism, which was metal. It was going to be an exhausting and noisy day.

It was an exhausting day. Numbers 2 and 3 platoons were to take the brunt of the assault, and number 1 platoon would be in support.

My section formed up, in a gulley. The target was not now in sight. We were briefed by the section leader. We were to proceed along the gulley, bringing us closer to the foot of the hill. We would then form up, ready for the assault.

The cloud had thickened and it started to rain. As we lay in the undergrowth, the rain pattered off our scrim-covered helmets and found its way down our necks. The undergrowth was wet and was becoming muddy.

'Keep your rifles under cover, men,' called out Corporal Jelfs.

Yes, you must keep your best friend dry! I grinned to myself. 'Wish I had a best friend at the moment,' I thought.

Firing started over on the felt. This was the 'dummy' assault, by number 3 Platoon – the real graft was for number 2!

My section had a target to reach, on the right hand side of the hill.

'Bren gun, right flanking, follow me!' bawled Lance Corporal Edge. The bren gun team set off, having collected some magazines from the riflemen.

Soon, a rat-tat-tat of firing came from the bren group. Corporal Jelfs waved his sub-machine gun.

'Section, left flanking, follow me!' he cried, and set off.

The going got harder as we jogged forward on rising ground. The water gurgled in my water bottle and my wet trousers clung to my knees. My feet were still dry, thanks to my anklets.

'Down!'

We flopped behind a small ridge. 'Twelve o'clock, two hundred, rapid fire,' screamed some maniac. We set up a hellish racket.

Over to the right, Lance-corporal Edge was hollering his bren

80

group forward. they could be seen making for a line of trees near the foot of the hill. As their rattle recommenced, the rifle group ceased firing and, on order, fixed bayonets.

Forward we went. We slogged up the hill, through the acrid, covering mortar smoke. I stumbled forward, and jogged by a still smouldering mortar bomb. Thunder flashes were being let off by strategically placed instructors. One exploded close by, making my ears sing.

Up the hill! In spite of the chill rain, the sweat was pouring off us as we crashed and staggered in ragged line, through the bushes, up to the top. Goaded on, we surged forward to assault the 'enemy' slit trenches, previously dug for the exercise, and the fox-holes. We leapt in through the smoke and noise, screaming like maniacs, and took over the position.

'Get up! – go forward! Go on! – forward, over the top, to consolidate! Go, on. Move!' Some zealot was yelling at us as we got up and pushed ourselves forward on to the opposite face of the hill, with our tortured lungs gasping for air.

'Right. Consolidate. Dig in.'

With the entrenching tools carried on our packs, we dug and scooped furiously. The holes were sited by the platoon commander, who suddenly appeared – Verey pistol in hand.

'Come on! Hurry up! You'll get your bloody heads blown off,' he rapped, as we dug away like moles.

Bullied and cajoled, we finally dropped into our holes in ones and twos and faced forward, looking as though we were braced and alert for the counter attack. The policy, always, was to move forward, away from the captured positions, as these were pin-pointed by enemy fixed line guns, and could be accurately blasted without trouble.

Lieutenant Watkins, water dripping off his nose, now fired the Verey pistol to signify the completion of the mission. Down below, in company H.Q. behind a thicket, Major Smythe looked at his watch.

'Not good enough, yet, sergeant-major,' he snapped. 'We shall have to sharpen them up.'

'Yes, sir,' replied the CSM. 'They'll be pretty good, sir, in another six months.'

'They'll have to be bloody good!' was the short reply.

We took what shelter we could, and ate our lunch. A pick up truck had come along the lane, up a track, and was parked. Dixies of tea were brought out. This was a bit of a bonus, and very welcome. However, the haversack rations still had to be faced.

The weather improved.

The officers and NCOs had another 'O' group, to work out the scheme for the afternoon.

Quite simply, the programme was a forced march to a complex of flooded gravel pits, small rivers and a canal, where other flanking exercises, involving the 'leap-frogging' of rifle and bren groups, would take place.

The sections marched down the verges of the side roads, staggered, in the approved manner. The pace was hot, and the troops reasonable cheerful; after all, we had eaten our haversack rations, and our clothes had dried out. We carried our rifles slung. We walked along like veterans, with our right thumbs hooked in the rifle slings. The bren gunners carried their weapons across their shoulders. The 2-inch mortars were not to be used again, and mercifully they had been loaded on to the P.U.

I legged along behind the section corporal. The men were well spaced out and alert for any cry of 'Aircraft' or 'Take Cover', which would send them instantly to ground. We were sharp – perhaps not yet sharp enough, according to Major Smythe – but standards were exacting. The company commander was well aware that many of these young soldiers were the patrol leaders and section commanders of the future – the future when the war would take a turn, as the Army was going to have to punch its way across Europe. If this bloody war was going to be won, boys like these would have a big stake in it.

We pushed on through a couple of small villages. The women and children watched from the gates as we swung easily by, with our scrimmed helmets, mud-spattered clothes and dirty faces. We said little, but we grinned at the kids and waved at the women.

We saw water, glinting in the wan winter sun in the spaces between the trees and bushes lining the road. We were halted and took cover, while NCOs went forward to recce the target.

My section fell for the right-flanking, round-a-bout sweep to approach the platoon target, which was a concrete construction containing disused, gravel-grabbing machinery. The target area, hopefully, was clear of village kids, most of whom were still at afternoon school. The area had been reccied and red flags had been put up by the CSM travelling ahead in the PU.

The right-flanking movement took our section up a sluggish ditch. In we went, the water lapping our denims, just making us really wet, as we churned forward. The river stank of rotting vegetation; some gnats found their targets, even though it was winter, and oily, muddy bubbles welled up from the depths as we waded forward.

Puffing and sweating, we dragged out of the ditch and took up positions, well below the steep bank and now in close proximity to the target. Across our front flowed a river. There was a small footbridge.

Lieutenant Watkins came from the left and flopped down by Corporal Edge.

'Right, corporal; from here, it is a frontal assault for this section, to tackle that concrete building. Covering fire is by bren and rifles of number 1 section. You can't use the foot-bridge, as it is under fire, and probably booby-trapped. You will move in five minutes, when I blow two blasts on the whistle,' he concluded.

'What stupid sod thought this one up.' muttered Bill Perks, the rifleman next to me. 'Straight across the bloody river, an' me mum told me not ter get me feet wet.' He grinned, wryly. 'If the ol' dear saw me, now, she'd 'ave bloody kittens!'

'Right, fellers,' said the corporal, 'when the blast goes off, run like 'ell; keep spread out; don't bunch, or 'ang abart on the bank – get over. Watch out for the thunder flashes – I see the bloody sergeant sneak off over that way a few minutes ago.'

'Right, Go!' The whistle blasts brought us up to our feet, rifles held, in both hands, across our chests. We stumbled across the rough scrub to the river. As we dropped down the bank, the thunder flashes went off. The sergeant was really going to town! The noise was deafening. A few bakelite grenades were tossed into the fray. A thunder flash exploded in the water, then a grenade shot a spout up. As I dropped down into the swirling river, I saw a number of roach and dace floating by, up-side down. We dragged ourselves up the opposite bank and raced forward, yelling like demons amid the smoke and the noise. We completed the assault and took up positions, forward of the building. By now, the light was going. We were called to order and lined up by platoons.

I recognised the spot where we assembled. Thank God, we were not far from camp!

'Number 2 platoon, double march.' The order was yelled by the platoon officer, and the men, cold and wet as they were, thankfully broke into the double. We jogged along the road, wet, muddy and pretty shattered. Back to the main road we went, – along it for a mile or so, and then left, down the road towards camp, our boots clumping in unison, the platoon sergeant at the side calling the step.

We were none too early. It was rapidly getting dark, and traffic was building up. The natives looked on in awe as the platoons doubled by, one after the other. As we approached the camp, we were halted. We then sloped arms, and marched smartly up the last road.

The rest of that particular evening was spent in hot showers, hot evening meal, and kit scrubbing and blancoing, ready for an inspection, on the following day.

Chapter Seven

My seven days' leave was due two weeks before Christmas. I would then spend Christmas Day in camp, as there was to be no Christmas leave. These were difficult times, and a soldier going on leave took most of his kit and his rifle. This was so that he was ready to muster at any local point, as required, should there be an invasion.

I regarded the forthcoming leave with mixed feelings. Of course, it would be great to get away from the exacting routine of the camp, and to be able to relax. It would be good to spend some time at the works, and see mates I had sometimes missed during the last few weeks. I had already seen my parents several times, now that I was so near home.

I had bought a small regimental brooch for my mother. I had also bought a second to send to Stella. She would be in good company, as there were quite a few of the Cheshire ladies proudly wearing similar favours, bestowed on them by their London sweethearts.

Having collected leave pass, travel warrant and ration card, I kitted up, took my rifle, and set off for the main road and the bus.

I just made it, as the hourly bus was pulling away from the kerb. I ran after the slowly-moving vehicle, and leapt on to the platform. I grabbed at the rail with my left hand, as my rifle was in the other one. The weight of my large pack upset my centre of gravity, but as I tottered backwards I was seized by the conductor and pulled safely aboard.

The journey was without incident. I walked the last part, and, opening the gate, went up the drive. I cluttered in through the back door, and wriggled out of my pack.

'Hello, Mum!' I shouted.

Is that you, George?' She came to the door of the living room as I came in, dragging my pack and carrying my rifle. She looked at the gun with some slight trepidation. She hadn't seen a rifle before, and to see me holding one as though it were part of me took her aback for an instant. Of course she knew that my stock in trade was guns and bullets, but it had not been brought home to her in such a brutal manner before.

I put the gun in the corner, and undid the pack, taking out my change of clothing.

'Mum, here's me ration card, 'I said, handing over the green paper, marked with squares and crosses; 'I arranged for a vegetarian one, like you said, to get more cheese. Oh, 'an I've brought you this.'

'Ooh, that's nice,' she said, admiring the neat, enamelled badge, with the pin at the back. She bustled round to make a cup of tea.

I took a stroll round the garden. It was neat and tidy, with the grass cut short, and the edges neatly trimmed. I came indoors as it started to drizzle, while the pylons in the neighbouring field hissed in the rain.

I went up to the little bedroom where I had spent so many hours at study, and changed out of uniform. I came down to a cup of tea and some toast.

'We'll have some tea when yer father comes home. Him an' Brian get home at about the same time. Your dad doesn't work quite such long hours now he's an instructor.'

Mr Milton had recently been seconded from his factory to work in a government training centre, teaching girls the crafts required to take over from the men. He had proved to be a good instructor of boy trainees for some years, so it was a sensible move. He still cycled to work.

Brian came in first.

'Hallo,' he said in greeting. 'I told them at work you were coming home today. Said you might be in tomorrow.'

'Yeh, OK,' I replied, casually. 'I'll look in in the morning. I hope to visit school, too, in the afternoon. Shan't come home, Mum; I'll have something at the British Restaurant.'

Shortly after this, my father arrived home. It was plain that he was not so tired these days, since he had changed his job. The pressure of aircraft production had been lifted from his shoulders. He was in a cheerful mood.

While supper was being prepared, I showed Brian my rifle, and explained the workings of it. Then, even though I was in shirt sleeves, I was prevailed upon to demonstrate the standard movements of arms drill – the slope, the order; the present arms, and butt salute; the port arms, for inspection. They were all duly impressed. My mother looked on with what seemed to me like miserable foreboding when I showed them the shorter, fluted bayonet, and how it was fixed to the barrel. Although I made light of the whole thing, I couldn't of course deny the fact that it was not a game we were playing.

After supper, we sat around the fire. The coal ration was eked out with logs, collected by Brian and my father. We talked about wooding, and sawing logs – a job that I had enjoyed in the past.

'There's a big 'un, down the road,' said my father. 'It was a bit too much for me the other night, but I reckon we could manage it between us.'

'Let's go and see,' I said quickly, anxious to find an excuse to break away from my mother's glances. The atmosphere had become very slightly strained since the bayonet demonstration.

'Oh, I shouldn't bother,' said my mother. 'Perhaps Brian can help one night.' Brian had gone out to a friend's in the village.

'No, come on; it'll make a nice change,' I pressed. 'We've done some chucking about of logs recently, in P.T.' I went on to explain how we had carried out drill movements, where lines of six men had swung these large smooth trunks of wood from shoulder to shoulder over our heads – and so on. I also explained the weight lifting exercises we did, lifting and swinging our heavy rifles, holding them at the end of the barrel, to develop muscle tone.

'It's only down by the corner,' said my father. We took a masked flash light, and set off. Reaching the spot on the edge of the copse, I shone the light, cautiously. My father dragged out a medium sized bough.

'That bugger's a bit too big,' he said, directing my beam to a much larger limb.

'You take that one, an' I'll take this one,' I said, in what I hoped sounded a matter-of-fact way. I had lifted the end of the big limb, and assessed it. It would be O.K., once I got it on my shoulder, at the point of balance.

'Don't be so bloody silly – you can't take that,' exclaimed father; 'I wouldn't even want to carry one end.'

I handed the torch over. I rolled the bough round for a better grip, and lifted one end. Walking under it, I manoeuvred to the point of balance, carefully straightened my bent legs, and hoisted it on to my shoulder.

'Christ, it is bloody heavy!' I thought as I raised it off the ground. Father looked on, stupified, as I set off with a steady rhythm, taking care not to let the bough swing sideways, or dip to hit the ground.

My father followed, carrying a smaller piece of timber. I could see that he was trying to come to terms with a new situation. He was a hard, physically energetic man, although a lung injury gave him breathing problems when under exertion. He now found himself with a Frankenstein in the family, in the shape of a son who had grown and developed physically to a capability that he could no longer match.

We made our way home, where I slipped my burden with a neat jerk, on to the lawn. We went indoors and cleaned up.

'Did you get it?' asked Mum. I said nothing.

'Silly bugger fetched a bloody trunk home, on his own,' exclaimed my father, still only half believing what had happened. 'You shouldn't do that,' she replied, with concern. 'You'll hurt yourself.'

I had to see the droll side of the situation – thinking of the drill, the running, the assault courses; the long trots across country, loaded up; the flanking movement, down the filthy, wet ditch, and that surge across the river, only last week – and I grinned, as I reassured her. 'S'alright, Mum, I have had to carry a lot of loads lately, and I suppose I've got used to it.'

I could sense my father looking at me as I sat in an upright chair, and I was conscious that he was sizing me up – aware that I had become stronger and tougher, that the training had hardened me up, and the boniness was filling out.

'Look what he brought me,' said Mum, showing off the brooch; 'I shall wear that to work, when I get back next week.' She had managed a few days' leave, to coincide with some of mine.

My father admired the brooch, with its regimental crest and 'Albuhera' scrolled across the base.

'I bought two,' I said, without thinking.

'Oh – who's the other one for, then?' came the inevitable question from my mother.

I couldn't help looking confused. I had never had to discuss girls with them, before.

'Oh, a girl I know, in Chester – Stella, is her name,' I replied, affecting as casual a tone as I could manage.

'You kept 'er a bit quiet,' she replied. What's she like then?'

'Oh, she's nice; you'd like her,' I said.

My father looked interested – and, yes, amused. To him this was another surprise development.

'A North Country girl, eh?' she asked.

'Yes,' I said, with a laugh, 'I suppose she is.'

My parents exchanged glances, full of unanswered and unanswerable questions; questions they didn't know how to pose, and I certainly wouldn't know how to answer!

How long have you known her, then?' asked Dad, with interest.

'Oh, quite a while,' I said dismissively, not wanting them to know what a short time it had been.

'Does she write, then?' asked Mum.

'Yes, she does,' I replied; 'I hope to go and see her one weekend.'

'Where would you stay?' queried my mother, while my father sat, plainly amused, with disbelief showing on his face.

'There's a lady in the town, does bed and breakfast for our chaps. She's a widow, an' she would find room for me.' I found this quizzing irksome, but funny also. Clearly my mother didn't know, or didn't want to know, the sort of wicked world that existed outside the village.

'Oh,' was all she said.

The next day, I smartened up, and caught a bus to visit the old firm. I was, of course, in uniform. Brian had warned them that I was coming, so that I should not have a major security problem at the gate.

I went round the labs where I used to work. It was all the same. It was nice to go back and tell my mates how life was treating me, but I didn't find the yearning to return that had plagued me when first I returned South.

Two of my old mates were keen young home guards, who had been taught a few tricks. I was able to show them something of the extent of my unarmed combat skills.

Pauline came into the prep. room, where a few of them were clustered around me. Pauline was a girl I used to admire, from a distance. She worked in the Research Manager's office, and she swayed her shapely hips around the building with the sophistication of a girl who knew how to use her assets. I had never really spoken to her, being much too shy, but she gave a start of surprise, when she saw me.

'Oh, hello,' she chirped.

'Hello, Pauline,' I replied, with an ease that surprised me. 'I've been dreaming about you, ever since I've been away.'

'Go on, you!' she exclaimed but she blushed, and was momentarily confused. She was too surprised to think of anything else to say. She certainly hadn't expected such sauce from the George Milton whom she had known around the labs.

They all chuckled loudly as she retired.

'You're a cheeky sod these days, George,' said Pete Rowley, one of my old mates. 'Shouldn't be surprised if you didn't get a date there. She won't give any of us a tumble. If that's what the bloody Army does for yer, I'd better sign on tomorrow.'

'Have to see what I can manage,' I said with a laugh. I knew that I had spoken in the security of the crowd. I was fully aware that I should be completely at a loss if I was confronted by the young lady alone.

I had my lunch at the British Restaurant that I knew of. I had often been here when at work, and it was still the same utility fare, but it was cheap.

In the afternoon, I visited my old grammar school. It was handy to the works. Although I remembered the place as a tough, hard-work school, they were nearing the end of term, and things were slacker. I met my old headmaster, who had won an MC with Allenby, and I did the rounds of the rest of the (all male) staff. It was a rather subdued affair. Most of the masters were survivors of the 1914-18 war. I remembered that each Armistice Day, a horrifyingly long list of old boys who had been killed in that war of attrition, used to be read out. It was already apparent to the staff that the list would be a good bit longer before this lot was settled. The school had already lost quite a few – mostly air crew. The head had announced the latest casualty at assembly that very morning. An old boy, who I had known, had been shot down in a raid off the coast of Italy.

I caught a bus home – the same bus that I had caught in the old days. I sat at the back, and nobody recognised me. The bus wended its way through the orchards, into the village, out again, and home.

They asked me at home what sort of day had it been, and I told them the snippets.

The rest of my leave passed very quickly. I went to a dance or two, where I met a few mates, and I had a few drinks. It was all very quiet. It had, however, been long enough to be unsettling, and I thought of my return to the harsh routine with a certain trepidation.

Chapter Eight

As I expected, I found camp hard to adjust to. My longing to be with Stella came flooding back. I sent her the brooch for Christmas, with a long letter telling her about my leave and how desperately I wanted to see her.

Christmas came and went. The Army tried its best to unbend, and made a fair job of it.

At dinner, the officers served the men, as was the custom, and they did it well. Plates of poultry and pork, with all the trimmings, were washed down with china mugs of beer, poured by the officers from brimming buckets. The NAAFI was bedecked with chains and mistletoe, and the NAAFI girls, and any venturesome ATS, had a torrid time – the lads seemed to vie with each other who could manage the longest, most passionate and most melting kiss. Some of the girls came up gasping for air.

I had a quiet time with the family on Boxing Day.

Time flew.

In the spring, I was transferred to HQ company, to study a morse, Don 5 and wireless operator's course. This meant a move to a new hut, over the other side of the camp.

Life here was different. My new hut was equipped with single beds – if you can call three smooth planks resting inches off the floor on wooden cross pieces, a bed. The hut was much more relaxed than the 'B' company one, and there wasn't time for the fierce Saturday competition. It was occupied by HQ staff – signals, regimental police, orderlies and the like.

Most of the early days were spent mastering the morse code, Don 5, signal flags and the portable wireless set. It still wasn't easy. Lectures and practice were gruelling, and later I was to find that doubling across country with an 18 set on my back could be tough.

About this time, permission came through for me to go to the evening classes, as promised by the education sergeant. Apart from the change, it sometimes meant being excused guards or late duties, as the Army were very sensitive about such education privileges. I went along to the polytechnic, about three miles up the road to the east of the town. My arrival, for chemistry and physics, caused a flutter the first week, but they soon got used to me. I found the work difficult, as I had lost touch, and it was getting on for a year since I had last done this. I caused a big initial flutter in the breast of Joan. Joan was seventeen, pretty, clever, and fascinated by being confronted with an infantry soldier, proudly wearing his regiment blazoned across both shoulders; an infantry soldier, who could study at this level. There was a feeling among many of the civilian population – and indeed, in the services, too – that anyone with brains would be in some technical arm, and that only the hard and brainless cases became infantry soldiers. This was a pity, because the infantry soldier had to be able to dabble in the skills of many of the technical arms – he had to be able to act as a mechanic, a signalman, an engineer; he had to be able to clear a way through a minefield, if necessary, to service a motor vehicle, to repair simple faults in radio.

Anyway, there was I, causing a stir with this young lady student. Unashamedly, as the only girl in the class, she sat by me and partnered me in experiments. It was nice to be a potential hero, while it lasted, but she was a fickle young lady, when she found that I was a very ordinary young man who wasn't likely to threaten any minor risk or excitement, she deserted me for her former civvy class mate.

There was another event of note at that time – an event which was to lead to a long and memorable friendship that only ended on a traumatic note that is not for this story. The event was the appearance of Bob Eldridge. Bob was from Battersea. He was a likeable, cheerful lad, full of banter and high spirits. He was small but lively, and he was on the signal cadre too, having been transferred from one of the other companies. He had come down from Chester on the same draft as me, but our paths had never crossed till now. We partnered each other on some of the communication exercises, and we occasionally went for a drink. During break periods, we went to the NAAFI together.

It was early one evening, and we had finished the afternoon of morse and wire splicing. There was, inevitably, some larking about – all good natured – and I was engaged in a verbal exchange with a couple of the lads.

'Oi, watch it; 'e's me mate! Leave 'im be, or we'll sort the bloody lot of yer, out!' came the breezy interruption.

The banter went on, all in good fun. The incident, however, had quite an effect on me. I had never been highly popular at school, although I had been an athlete, and I hadn't really been the life and soul of anyone's party since – yet this bloke from a tough part of London, a bloke whose whole background of pre-Army experience, was so different from my own, had singled me out as his special buddy. Our contact had not been especially close within the group. Yet do or die, it seemed we were now stuck with each other. For a while, it left me vaguely ill at ease, hoping that I could live up to this confidence and trust placed in me. I hadn't been used to such a responsibility before.

While I was learning my trade, I kept in touch with my old mates

91

of the infantry companies. Their training and preparation was becoming more and more demanding. They went out on day-long exercises, which became progressively more arduous, and they came back very tired, with cuts and bruises to be treated, and filthy equipment to be cleaned. Not that HQ company dodged it all. Like the others, we had to complete a pretty tough infantry programme, which included the dreaded all-day route march. This was a thirty-miler. The troops all made certain that, above all else, their socks were in good condition – a blister on the heel after about five miles, didn't bear thinking about.

We checked and adjusted our equipment, we dubbined our boots, and we 'soaped' our socks.

We started off early one morning, and, swinging along, marching at platoon strength, were soon into our stride. It was a fine day. A young second lieutenant, whose name I did not know, was in charge, and a corporal signals instructor was the senior NCO. The route lay eastwards, in a wide arc east of Hounslow.

We were in a cheerful mood. With a ten minute break in every hour, it all seemed cushy enough. The first part of the route took us through Feltham. As we approached the village, and, regretfully, passed *The Airman* hostelry, the officer hastily ordered us to 'march to attention'. He didn't want to risk our rendering of *I don't want to join the Army* to offend the natives. From here, we struck south east, and crossed the river. We were still in a care-free mood. Between areas of population, all along the lanes and by-roads of Surrey, we were able to sing our ditties, and the officer tolerated the refrain when he felt that the density of population was low enough to risk offence.

We stopped every hour for a ten minute halt, when we stretched out on the grass verges, with equipment loosened. It was great, to lie back, head resting on your pack, and watch the light clouds go scudding overhead. The real war seemed years away. I tried to imagine what it was going to be like when these were French and Belgian roads, and we would be resting, like this, waiting to move against a strong point or a village – with no known billet at the end of the day.

We passed Walton, Teddington, Kingston, where we stopped for the midday hour, on a wide verge with brushwood and scrub, on one side of the road. Many of us disappeared for a 'jimmy'. We ate most of our rations and drank sparingly from the water bottles.

We reassembled. I was in the offside file, with a good view of the route, with Bob Eldridge on my inside. We had quietened down quite a bit, as blisters had begun to form, and soreness was creeping in feet and buttocks.

'Bloody 'ell, my arse is sore!' complained the man in front of me. At the next halt, vaseline was produced by the more far-sighted among us, and this was dispensed generously. It worked, for a while. The singing had largely died down – many of the marchers were gritting their teeth, and the strain was beginning to show in sweat-grimed faces. The corporal shouted the time, on occasions, to keep us in step. Some of those with energy left helped by calling out the time.

'Left, Left. Had-a good- job an' – I Left!'

Richmond was next. We passed by the 'Poppy Factory' – home of some of the maimed of the previous war. Some of the more imaginative – or more morbid – could not help wondering about their own chances of ending up in a place like that. We crossed back over the river, at Twickenham. We marched on – taking our hourly breaks – becoming more stiff and tired with every mile.

By about 3.30 we were approaching Hounslow, from the south east. We were very weary, and the marching was beginning to get ragged. As we came to the outskirts of the town, we had our last halt.

'Cor, look, George.' Bob pointed down the road, in the direction we were to take. Marching along the opposite side, was a drum and fife detachment from the barracks. They were swinging along, easily, to the tap of a drum. They came to a halt near the forward platoon. The other platoons had closed up, so that the rabble was at company strength.

'Right, men,' called out the leader of the forward platoon; 'we're going through the centre of town, an' you'll march to attention – no singing! Straighten up! There isn't far to go, an' they've brought the band out for you.'

So they had. It wouldn't do for us to march in scruff order, through our home town. Regimental honour, no less, was at stake.

We marched back, platoon by platoon, behind the fife and drums. The musical support had a magical effect. Aching limbs eased and overburdened shoulders were straightened as we swung through the High Street, to the western limits. We could make it now – and in style. We swathed our way through town with heads held high, and a new spring in our step. The shoppers and trademen paused and stared, agape, as we soldiers marched proudly through the home town.

After welcome showers and a hot meal, the evening was spent in treating blisters and sores. Few went even as far as the NAAFI that night.

Time went on, with little change in the hard and uncompromising routine of the unit. Spring developed into early summer, and it was difficult not to be cheerful, in spite of it all.

The Sunday after the march, my platoon was detailed to parade for inspection for church. We lined up and were duly inspected by the duty officer before we marched off. The inspection took a little longer than usual – there were one or two fiddling delays – and we had to wait about. In the meantime, the sun had burst forth, and that meant trouble. Like many others, I had taken a 'short cut'. Instead of treating my best boots with dubbin, as was the strict order, I had coated them with a good layer of boot blacking, left unpolished. The appearance was the same, but there wasn't the dirt and inconvenience of the grease.

The officer was in a bad mood. He paced along our rows, in open order for the inspection. He came along the front row a second time, and stopped opposite me. He fixed me with a baleful stare, and I had a sense of foreboding.

'Private, what have you dressed your boots with?' he rasped.

I glanced down at my feet and saw, to my horror, that my boots had started to shine. We had been out in the sun, just too long. The game was up.

'Sergeant, take that man's name, and put him on a charge.'

That is how 034, Private Milton, G., incurred his first dose of five days' CB – for having Army boots that were too shiny!

Company orders was a chastening experience. I paraded, on Monday morning, in best BD, boots (dubbined) and gaiters. The parade of miscreants and escorts was carefully inspected by the CSM.

When my turn came for summary justice, I found myself lined up, ready to march into the company commander's office. In front of me was a lance-corporal escort, and the sergeant who had charged me was behind. The CSM barked into life.

'Prisoner, hat off! Prisoner and escort, quick march! Left, right, left, right, left . . .'

Up the steps we marched, into the office, and in front of the company commander's desk.

'Mark time! Pick those feet up! Left, right, left . . .' Deta-i-l, halt! Right turn! Escort, stand-dat-tease!'

The march into the office had been traumatic. I was bemused by orders being bellowed at close range in a confined space, and the sergeant's knees, almost up my backside, had virtually propelled me into the office.

The five days was a graft! After my usual duties, which were tough enough anyway, I spent the next hour on the square, being drilled by the provost sergeant. After this, it was an evening of fatigues. The first night, I was detailed to wash mountains of greasy pans in the cookhouse. Another night, I peeled countless sacks of potatoes – or so it seemed. After duties, I had to rush back to change into BD, to report to the guard room for the lowering of the flag, and the bugle. In the mornings, I rushed down to report at reveille.

Still, I was free by the weekend, and I hadn't spent much money.

94

Stella hadn't written quite so often lately, and I guessed she was busy. One morning, I was delighted to get a letter with the familiar, back-sloping writing on the envelope. I sat on my blanket stack, and tore it open. She told me the news, such as it was, and asked what chance was there of my coming up pretty soon, as she was very anxious to see me. God, didn't she believe that I was anxious to see her, and that I would wangle time, whenever it was possible! I had already thought that I had a fair chance of being granted a short leave, and I decided to apply, in writing, to the company commander.

I decided to apply for the following weekend. It was granted – at least, it was granted in part. I could go on Friday afternoon, but I would have to return on Saturday night, as there was a 'stand by' on Sunday. Although this was a bit less than I had hoped for, there seemed little chance of a better offer for some time, as exercises were pending.

I checked my train times, and caught the express from King's Cross. Arriving in Chester, I looked around for Stella. She had arranged to meet me at the station, and she had booked for me to stay the night with Mrs Jones, the widow who catered for the lads with bed and breakfast.

I passed through the barrier, and saw her waiting by the entrance. I felt suddenly shy. I had been away for some time, and I was going to have to start from 'cold' – not an easy thing for me to do. She looked a bit different from how I had pictured her.

'Hallo, darling,' I said awkwardly, and kissed her on the cheek – her lips didn't seem to be available.

'Hallo, George, how are you?' she said, diffidently. 'I've fixed for you to stay with Mrs Jones – we had better go and see her, first.'

'Sure; OK,' I said, gruffly. I took her arm, and we wended our way the short distance to my lodging. Stella still seemed awkward and ill at ease. 'Poor girl,' I thought. 'She's shy, as well. Never mind; that will soon sort itself out, after a few drinks.' Even so, I felt a bit flat.

Mrs. Jones came to the door when I knocked. She knew Stella of course, and she welcomed me with a smile. She showed me to my room while Stella waited in the hall. I promised not to be late, thanked her, and left, escorting Stella through the front door.

'She's nice,' I said.

'Yes, she is, isn't she,' came the reply . Stella gave me a smile, and took my arm.

'Where shall we go, then?' I asked, rather expecting that we should go to her place; but apparently this was not the plan. Instead of going to *The Jolly Boatman*, I decided on the luxury of *The Grosvenor*.

I bought drinks and we sat down in the corner of the lounge, on plush seats. Suddenly, I felt shy again. To try to break the indefinable reserve between us, I rambled on about training, the marches and the assault course. She asked me what the town was like, and what I did in my spare time. Somehow, her mind seemed elsewhere, and I got a funny feeling that she was making conversation. I told her, with a grin, that my social life was restricted, because there wasn't anybody there like her.

She smiled, faintly. She certainly seemed to be taking a while to relax and shed her cloak of reserve. I got another drink. She began to thaw a bit, and I thought she looked very nice, with a summery dress and a pretty cardigan. She undid the cardigan, and I looked for the brooch that I had sent her for Christmas, but she wasn't wearing it. I felt disappointed, but I dare not ask any questions.

She put her glass, gently, on the table. There had been a pause in the conversation.

'George,' she began, 'I've got some news for you. . .' She stopped again.

'What is it, darling?' I asked, puzzled by the turn of events. 'You haven't got another bloke, have you?' I added, with a chuckle.

She laughed, but uncomfortably – not as I had expected.

'I think I'd better tell my story, George, in my own way.' I began to feel a sense of unease.

'It isn't going to be easy,' she went on; 'I particularly wanted to see you, because I have got something to tell you, and I didn't want to write it, in a letter.' She paused for breath.

I sat very still. My throat felt suddenly dry, in spite of the drink, and I felt an odd remoteness, almost as though I was an onlooker, outside of my own body – a listener-in.

She bit her lip, and took a firm grip on her glass, on the little table between us.

'It was not too bad at first,' she went on. 'I went out with the girls, and we had a laugh. I missed you, and I felt miserable , but I managed.' She paused again.

I drank silently from my glass.

She went on. 'You know where I work. Well, this boy – Tony, his name is – he used to come into the office. He was a laugh. He works across the road, in the other office. Well, he asked me to go out for a drink. I told him about you, but he said he understood, and that we could just go out, as friends. Well, it got to be a habit, and we both looked forward to it.' She paused, again. 'Oh, dear,' she said, 'it's very difficult.'

I spoke at last. My voice sounded rough in my ears, as though my throat was sore.

'Don't be upset, Stella. You can tell me the rest – if there is any more.' I suddenly felt a lot older. In a way, I felt in charge of the situation, although what she was saying was sending my dreams crashing in ruins.

She went on, somewhat encouraged by my line. 'Well, there is, George. I've got to like him rather a lot. Last Thursday, he came in while mum was at whist. That was when we realised, George.' Her eyes were full of tears.

I knew the rest before she told me. I felt numbed. The whole situation seemed unreal.

She went on again. 'He feels awful about you, George, but it isn't his fault. It just happened. Oh, George, I feel so awful.'

'Oh, ah. I'm sure he's very upset about me,' I exclaimed bitterly, before I could control my tongue.

She started to cry, the tears coursing down her cheeks.

I tried to think of something to say — something that would help. I tried to make amends.

'I'm sorry, Stella; that was a stupid thing to say. Don't cry. These things happen, and he isn't to blame.' I patted her hand, awkwardly.

'I suppose it's my fault, then,' she sobbed.

'No, I didn't mean that, you silly girl,' I protested. Why does a girl so often seem to put you in the wrong. 'Come on, things aren't that bad; he's a nice chap, isn't he?'

She dried her eyes, and looked at me hopefully.

'Oh yes, George; he's a very nice boy. I think it's the real thing, George.'

Even in my misery I felt like smiling at this dramatic utterance. She sounded a bit like Merle Oberon.

'Oh, and I thought, perhaps, you'd like me to give you this back,' she said. She drew the regimental brooch from her handbag, and offered it to me. I took it, clumsily, and thrust it into my pocket. I couldn't think of anything to say. For an awful moment I half expected her to give some old line about finding some nice girl one day to give it to.

'Look, Stella,' I said. 'Don't worry. I hope you will be very happy. I just want to wish you Good Luck.'

She looked down at her glass, and I could see that she was crying.

'Come on; let me see you home,' I said, decisively.

We got up and went out. It was a fine evening. We made our way along Station Road. I escorted her to her gate, for the last time. Holding her two hands, I squeezed them gently, and said, 'Good-bye, and good luck, Stella,' and then I went.

There was nothing else for it, but to go back to Mrs, Jones's. I made my way in, and found her making cocoa in the kitchen.

She looked up in surprise as I came in.

'My, you're early! Haven't had a lover's tiff, I hope.' she said, not knowing how hard she was making it for me to keep on an even keel.

'No, nothing like that Mrs. Jones,' I managed to reply. 'Stella isn't very well, and she's having an early night. I shall see her, tomorrow.'

'What a shame!' she exclaimed, putting two and two together, and making five! 'And the weekend you've come up, from London too!'

I declined her offer of a cup of cocoa, and went up to my room. I undressed and crawled beneath the sheets. My mind was in a whirl. The events of the evening, and the happy moments with Stella in the past, swam before my eyes. I could not sleep. The bitterness of the whole situation then overcame me, and I wept, silently, into my pillow. Then I slept, fitfully, until the early hours, when habit became too powerful to allow me to sleep on. I lay in bed for a while, but I felt so restless that I got up and dressed. I packed my case and went downstairs, where Mrs Jones was already installed in the kitchen.

'You are an early bird!' she exclaimed. 'Would you like your breakfast now?'

'I'll just have a cup of tea, if I may,' I said. 'I don't feel very hungry.'

I thanked her for putting me up, and then I managed to escape. I stayed calm while she rattled on, poor woman. It was going to be a fine day. So, what the hell! I wandered round for a while, from one end of the town to the other. I went as far as *The Jolly Boatmen*. There was the hawthorne bush where the trooper had been so busy. I passed the other pubs, and the dance hall where I had met Joyce. I made my way to the station and waited for the next London train. The morning was now well advanced. Suddenly, I felt so wretched and tired. My head seemed cold and numb, and I felt a roaring noise in the ears. I wandered towards the station buffet, but I didn't make it. Suddenly, the lights went out, and I was falling . . . falling.

'He's alright. Sit 'im up. Here, son; take a sip of this.'

A flask was thrust to my lips, and I felt the burning sensation of what I presumed was brandy, in my throat. I felt the blood rush back to my head, and shakily I got to my feet.

'OK, son.' A middle-aged man in a business suit took my arm and led me to a seat. He still had the hip flask in his hand. 'Where are you going?' he asked.

'I've got to catch the London train,' I said. 'I'll be OK now. Thanks for your help.'

They left me. I waited on the platform sitting on a seat with my head down.

When the train steamed in, I sat in the nearest carriage and just gazed out of the window. I did that all the way to London. I moved through the stations like a zombie. The Underground rattled me back to Hounslow. I walked into camp, and got to the hut in the late afternoon.

A few of the lads were cleaning up. It was immediately obvious to them, that I was in trouble. Gradually, they got the essentials out of me. Of course it was not a new story, but it made it no less sad. There was only one cure that the lads knew of in a case like this, and that was a 'bender', followed, ideally, by the open arms of some understanding lady of the town.

Bob came in. He had been on a visit to some of his old pals in the rifle company that he had been in.

'What-cher, cock!' he exclaimed, in pleasure. 'I didn't expect ter see yer back, so early. What's the matter – 'ave a row?' He suddenly shut up, and changed his tone, when he realised that something really was wrong. I sat at the hut table, and poured out the story to Bob. There wasn't much that Bob could say. Like the others, he thought that a 'bender' was the best immediate answer.

Something happened that denied the inmates of Hut 3, H.Q. company their 'bender'.

I had bucked up a bit under the ministrations of my mates. At that moment, local, acting, lance-corporal Page, regimental policeman, came in. He got the gist of the problem from the others. Page was not a popular man, even allowing for the limitations of his appointment. Today, he excelled himself.

'Why get upset over a bloody tart, you silly bastard,' he said, scornfully.

I froze.

He went on, inevitably. 'I expect her drawers have been pulled down as often as the bloody flag at the guard room!'

My control snapped at last. Standing up and reaching over the table, I punched L/cpl. Page, RP full on the mouth. The corporal fell backwards over the seat behind him, and hit his head on the floor. He stayed down, groaning. I felt strangely relieved. Sod 'em all! They could do what the bloody hell they liked.

A horrified mess waiter called in a passing corporal. He took one look, and hastily fetched the orderly sergeant. The inmates of the hut stood around silently as events took their inevitable course. The corporal went to sick bay. Bob and another private silently helped me pack my regulation small pack. The sergeant stood quietly by.

With kit packed, as required, I was escorted to the guard room, the sergeant conscripting two men from the hut as escort. We marched through the camp, in single file, to the curious stares of the troops we met. Such incidents were not common, but were sufficient to excite momentary interest – rather like the passing of a fire engine through the street. The sergeant of the guard duly received the prisoner, signed for me, in true Army fashion, and locked me in a cell.

I was past worrying too much about the consequences. My anger had evaporated, and so too had a lot of my heartaches, the new situation tending to over-shadow the former. I surveyed the accommodation. Concrete was the predominate theme. There was a wooden-based bed with blankets, and that was it. The room was about nine feet by eight feet, and the door was solid, with a peep hole.

'Would you like-a mugger tea?'

The voice sounded sympathetic. Surprised, I answered, 'Yes, please.'

A few minutes later, the sergeant came in, followed by one of the guard carrying a mug of tea. I sat on the bed, drinking the tea, while the sergeant quizzed me. They all knew L/cpl. Page, and he was distinctly unpopular. This, of course, did not lessen the gravity of the offence, but it did provoke some unofficial sympathy. The guard detail seemed a friendly lot. After the talk, I was left on my own again. As the evening advanced, the light came on, high up in the ceiling, switched on from outside the cell. At nine o'clock, they brought me some cocoa. I was escorted to the toilet, and then I was left to myself in my cell. With nothing else to do, I got undressed and into bed. To my surprise, I slept well.

The light stayed on.

Sunday was a long day. There were occasions, in the afternoon and early evening, when, irrationally, I wondered if they had forgotten me. I exercised round the very small, barbed-wire enclosure at the back of the guard room for about fifteen minutes. The guard had changed. It was a quiet time, and the guard commander let me out in the evening, to have my mug of cocoa with them. He also explained the procedure for the Monday morning, when I would be doubled up to the battalion HQ to face the camp commandant.

On Monday, shaved and carefully polished, I was doubled up to the battalion office. The procedure was similar to that for company orders, but on a grander scale. The escorts were RPs and the RSM marched the prisoner in, and preferred the charges.

The colonel looked up from his desk when the cavalcade had halted and the preliminaries had been gone through. He said nothing, for a moment, and then he gave me a shrewd stare.

'Mr. Jones,' he said, finally, turning to the RSM on my right, 'What can you tell me about the incident?'

'Well, sir,' said the RSM, in a voice of gravel, 'Lance/Cpl. Page has a headache, where he fell over, but we have his statement.'

'You mean, where Cpl. page was knocked over, don't you?' interrupted the commandant, icily. 'Private Milton, what have you got to say?' He looked at me, hard. 'Did you strike the corporal?'

'Yes, sir,' I replied, firmly.

'I see. Striking an NCO is a very serious offence,' said the officer.

'Yes, sir,' I replied.

'Well, what have you got to say?' he snapped.

I outlined, simply and without excuse, the remarks that had led up to the incident.

The colonel sat still and quiet. He could read between the lines of the statements and the evidence. He knew that I wasn't a bad soldier, and quite an intelligent one, and that, obviously, there had been some stress. He knew about the trip to Chester, and he was a very shrewd man. He guessed that there was a link, and he could not be very far from the truth. He had a fair idea that it was a case of 'the girl I left behind me', and such problems were not new to him.

At length, he turned to the RSM.

'Well, Mr. Jones, what is the situation?'

'Sir! It's true that the corporal is 'urt, sir; but 'e fell over a seat, and I think he was a bit unlucky, sir. He's alright, anyway. It's true that there was some provocation, sir.'

The RSM paused. I listened in surprise. I hadn't expected to hear any words of conciliation, especially from the RSM!

'I see.' The colonel thought for a while. It was a difficult one for him, but I was still a young soldier, and a promising one, and this carried the day.

'Have you anything else to say, Milton?' he said, finally.

'Yes, sir.' I hesitated. 'I am very sorry, sir. It was a stupid thing to do,' I added, lamely, 'I'm glad Cpl. Page is alright, sir.'

'I hope you are.' was the sharp retort. The officer went on. 'I am going to deal with your case myself, Private Milton. You could easily have been sent for a court martial.' He paused. 'As it is. . .' He paused again. 'I think you have been under some stress, and the corporal was unwise, to call you what he did. You, however, must learn to control yourself. We can't have you knocking our corporals about – understand?'

'Yes, sir,' I replied.

'Should such remarks be made to you in future, it is your duty to report them – not take the law into your own hands.'

'Yes, sir,' I said, knowing full well that the colonel didn't really expect me to take any such action.

The commandant turned again to the RSM.

'Anything else, Mr. Jones?' he asked.

'No, sir,' said the RSM. He could see how things were shaping, and he was satisfied.

'Ten days confined to barracks,' rapped the colonel.

The RSM instantly leapt into life.

'Left, right, left. . . .'

'Phew,' I thought, 'that was a let off!'

I changed into denims, and caught up with the platoon in the training hut, where they were working on their 18 sets. The message soon got round that I was on 'jankers'.

'Jus' goes to show; even the colonel knows what a burke that corporal is,' said Bob.

'Yeah; but George was dead lucky, all the same,' replied Chris Holt, another signaller.

Generally, it was agreed that things could have been worse.

'I suppose I'd better write to me Ma,' I said. 'Let them know why I won't be home next weekend.'

'I got a better idea,' said Bob. 'Me an' Chris 'ave bin talking it over. You don't live far away. Why don't we catch a bus one evening, an' we could tell your folks. You could easily tell us 'ow ter get there.'

I felt relieved and grateful. It would be so much easier for them to explain what had happened, not only over the charge, but also what had caused the upset – the break with Stella.

'Yeah, OK,' I said. 'Thanks.'

The following evening, Chris and Bob got away after tea. I completed a punishing session with the provost sergeant, and then had to go on NAAFI fatigue, collecting the empties, all evening. It wasn't a bad chore – there were worse.

By the time I had got back from the guard room, I was whacked. I got straight into bed, and I was fast asleep when they returned. However, they lost no time telling me all about it next morning.

They were full of the visit. My father had reacted to the visitors in the open-handed way that I had half expected, and, consequently, the lads had thoroughly enjoyed the trip. They had found the house without difficulty and arrived just after tea. They introduced themselves and gave my father a full account of the whole business, including the trip to Chester.

As expected, my father had been expansive and my mother had been worried.

'Well, I don't know,' my father had said. 'Do you mean to say that it's taken the Army nearly a year to find him out!' He had then marched them down to *The Fox,* and filled them up with rum.

'Cor, 'e's a right one, your dad,' said Bob. 'Bit of a lad, I'd say!'

'Yeh, he's OK,' I said. I thought to myself, 'If only they knew how things were, when he was in a bad mood, or not feeling very well; or just angry!'

The ten days passed, slowly, each day seeming like two, with the extra burden of punishment drills, parades and fatigues. One evening, the punishment drill, held just after tea, had been particularly arduous, and the quick marching, with the repeated changes of direction – 'right turn, left turn, about turn. . .' – had made one of the squad violently sick by the edge of the square. This was good luck for the rest, because the pace slackened during the remainder of the hour.

However, all things come to an end, and the time came when I was able to go down town with the boys for a drink. Needless to say, I had achieved a certain notoriety since the incident in the barrack room. Strange to say, little had been said at home when I next visited my parents.

The final act came some days later. I found a letter waiting for me on my blankets. I had just come in after trekking across country with an 18 set on my back. I noticed the Chester postmark, but I did not recognise the writing. I opened the envelope, puzzled and bemused.

'Oo's that from, then?' asked Bob, noticing my puzzled air. I opened the letter out, an read it. It was not a long one. Bob was watching me, and I could see his air of concern when he saw my face.

'Not bad news, mate?' he asked.

I said nothing. I sat down on the bench near the trestle table, the open letter beside me.

''Ere, you can read it for yerself,' I answered, gruffly and carelessly. 'There's nothing secret about it.'

'Oo's Pete Drage?' he asked.

'Oh, 'e was in our platoon, in PTW – joined the Cheshires. 'e's Stella's cousin, by the way. He's a good bloke.'

Pete had written from home, where he was on embarkation leave. He said that he was on fourteen days' leave, but we knew what that meant. It was the second part of the letter which caught Bob's eye.

'. . . She's expecting a baby . . . chap at work . . . getting married soon.'

So that was it! Poor Stella. I felt an almost overwhelming sympathy for her. No wonder she was so unhappy when I last saw her – she must have been worried sick. He must have done better than I did on the settee on a Thursday evening! She hadn't shaken her head, it seems, when Tony's hand had wandered under her skirt. Perhaps she had, the first time he tried it: perhaps Tony had shown more persistence. Perhaps she had expected me to try harder when she shook her head. Ah well, Tony obviously hadn't gone along prepared either, or she wouldn't have 'clicked'!

The words of the police sergeant who had once stopped me on the way back to camp, echoed in my ears.

'Mind she doesn't blame you for something you haven't done.'

Still, it was a mess. I decided to write, and give them both my very best wishes.

Chapter Nine

The unit was breaking up. The battalion was to be disbanded, and the young soldiers, now with a good background of training, were to go off to service battalions. Some were to go overseas, as replacements for units which had gone through the North Africa campaign, and were now poised to set foot in Europe, from the south. Others were to go to home-based battalions, to complete their training as units in the assault corps that was going to have to cut into Europe, from the north.

They were all going to infantry support units that they had enlisted for. Some of the boys had been training for many months in the rifle companies, and they were to be transferred to infantry battalions – many of them Scottish. They would fight under new colours. Towards the end of the summer, many of them had gone. Jim Dodson had gone, and so had John Lewin.

Finally, the last big batch was to go off to two service battalions of their own regiment – they were, in fact, to become the mortarmen and the machine gunners of the Second Army divisions.

The camp finally closed in July, leaving behind only a caretaker party. All we men were sent on ten days' leave, and detailed to report to a holding unit in Essex for a few short weeks before going to our service battalions in Kent, where so much of the build up of the Second Army was taking place.

I went off, on the bus home from camp, for the last time. I had handed in my rifle. Times had changed, and it was no longer considered necessary for troops to take rifles and kit home on leave. The threat of immediate invasion had disappeared. However, I had to take my kit home with me, as I was reporting to a new unit.

Arriving home, I let myself in. Everybody was at work. I changed into some civvies and wandered down to the village. I had my leave pay, supplemented by money that I had allotted home from my weekly pay, and which my mother had put by for me in the Post Office.

The atmosphere at home, had changed. I was no longer thought of as a boy. It was quite apparent that I had left boyhood behind. After all, apart from everything else, I had had to knock about away now for over a year. Sometimes my parents tried not to think of the manner in which I might have been completing my growing up. Maturity and experience came precipitately to many under such conditions.

I helped where I could at home. I made my rounds of calls, to work and school, but I was determined to spend time out on the town during this leave.

Uxbridge was quite lively, epecially at weekends. The national policy was for 'holidays at home', as travel was not encouraged, and many of the coastal resorts were restricted for military reasons.

There were many service people about, and in the evenings the pubs were crowded. During the course of my wanderings, I struck up a nodding acquaintance with others who were on leave, or stationed locally. Some of the taverns allowed for sing songs, and many a jolly evening was enjoyed with companions of the moment. On such occasions I walked the three miles home, so my head was usually cleared by the time I arrived. In any event, nobody stayed up for me. They all had jobs to do next day, and I was sensible enough to come in quietly.

One fine Saturday afternoon, I was strutting down to the outskirts of the town where a semi-permanent fun-fair was sited. I had come here fairly often at weekends while I had been stationed so handily. The fair was an obvious pick-up point for lonely servicemen, where they aimed to pair of with the local girls. The girls, too, were looking for some adventure to spice the bland routine of working life, and an involvement with a soldier posed a challenge that many of them readily accepted. In spite of the convivial, largely male drinking company, the pangs of loneliness were often acute, and the need to assuage these by winning a girl sometimes became desperately pressing. To me, the need was becoming ever more urgent. I had taken a few girls home from dances, and I had kissed most of them. I had then become trapped in the snare of friendship. I got talking to a girl about her life and interests, and then found it impossible to risk offending or disappointing her by making suggestions that might shock. To all and sundry, I presented an image of a fit, confident, predatory soldier, because my shyness and lack of experience or technique were not immediately obvious.

After much diffidence, I did manage to chat up one girl at the amusement park. I had been watching her for quite a while. She was younger than I had at first thought, as she had made valiant but amateurish efforts to put years on from a bottle. However, she went off willingly enough to the seclusion of the common in the gathering dusk, but she became pathetically scared of anything more than a kiss.

One fine afternoon during my leave, on the second Saturday and so toward the end, I was walking along the street towards the amusement park, resplendent in uniform, with regimental flashes, and distinctive red and yellow patches on my arms, when I came face to face with a solider coming out from a side street. We looked a each other. We both had the red and yellow flashes, and both wore our 'Middlesex' insignia, on our epaulettes.

'Hello,' I greeted, breezily, very pleased to meet a fellow 'Diehard', and knowing that he had not come from the 70th. 'Where are you stationed, then?'

'I'm at Chester,' answered the stranger, 'but were're on the move, soon. Where do you come from, then?'

I left Chester nearly nine months ago,' I told him. 'I'm in the 70th, but we've just broken up, and I'm off soon to join one of the battalions.'

His name was Bill Turley, and he lived just along the road. He too was on leave and would shortly be moving to a battalion. He was a bit younger than I was

We decided to pool resources. We were both aware that hunting was considered to be more successful when conducted in pairs. Working as a team, we both felt that we might make some better progress with the ladies of the town.

We toured the amusement park, trailing our coats, so to speak. Towards evening, we linked up with two ATS girls, who were stationed nearby. The girls were only too ready to join us for drinks, provided that we paid, and the evening soon turned out to be an expensive one. Later on, we took the girls back to their billet, which was in a large private mansion, with extensive grounds. Bill very soon made a blunt and direct approach, which left my ears singing and my nerves agog. I had to smile to myself when I thought of him as 'presenting the bill', after a dear night. I envied him the ability to tackle the girls in this fashion. In the most secluded spot that the girls could be manoeuvred to, he popped the question to his girl. He was promptly told that there was nothing doing. He cajoled and argued, but it was obvious to me that we were completely defeated, and that further discussion would be a waste of time. Me and my own partner, the other ATS girl, were spectators to the contest without taking any part in it. It was almost as if we were reserving our position, awaiting the outcome of the gladiatorial contest taking place in the arena before us.

Finally defeated – routed, in fact – my new buddy and I decided to meet again next day, Sunday, and try again. I agreed to call round for him, at his home on a larger estate, just on the outskirts of town.

I called next afternoon. Bill was putting the final polish to his boots.

''Allo; come in, mate,' called out a largish Mrs. Turley. ''E's nearly ready. You lads – yer worse than the girls fer tartin' yerselves up. Anybody'd think you was on parade instead of on leave.

We set off. It was a nice afternoon, and there was time to kill before the afternoon really got going, so we walked along the canal, watching the anglers and admiring the narrow boats. There was little prospect of rain, and we enjoyed taking the air. We bought a cup of tea and a bun in a little shop nearby that catered for the river and the canal trade. After this, we had another wander round. The streets were by now more populated, with the usual crowds of service types and the bevies of town girls. There were families in evidence, taking the afternoon air, and we sometimes had to move adroitly out of the line of small children.

We wandered round the all too familiar amusements, back-chatting the girls and trying to make some headway. When eventually we did succeed, it all seemed so easy. Two very attractive girls were walking along, casually chatting to each other and taking little or no notice of those around them. I should not have rated them as a 'chance', but Bill, with his less sensitive and uninhibited manner, cheekily accosted them.

'Hallo, you couple of smashers; what are you doing, all alone, then!' he said, as an introductory plunge.

The two girls looked at us, coolly. They were obviously unperturbed, and slightly amused. They carried on with their walk, past the cocoanut shy, and without positively encouraging us, they were not aloof. Encouraged by the fact that we had not been instantly rebuffed, we continued to tow along. Even though I was surprised by the turn of events, I was emboldened by the initial success, and I found myself joining in.

'If you aren't doing anything special, why not tag along with us,' I suggested. 'We're on leave.'

'Are you local boys, then?' asked the taller one. She was tall and attractive, with a graceful athletic build that drew me. I guessed her to be slightly younger than me, but she was quite self-assured.

'Yeah,' said Bill, 'I live in Bridge Lane, and George here lives two or three miles out of town.'

The other girl, who was much shorter and very blonde, said, 'Oh, I know where that is; I live about a mile from there.'

'Where's that then?' asked Bill, 'and how come I haven't seen a cracker like you about?'

She laughed. 'I've not long moved down to my auntie's, in Chaucer's Road, 'cause I work in the offices at Martins. Heather works there, as well.'

'Where do you live then, Heather?' I asked. By some apparently telepathic system, it was already established that I should pair up with Heather and that Bill would partner Blanche. The girls accepted us as escorts, and the evening scene was set. They were not like the usual pick-ups, being more attractive, neatly dressed and self-assured.

After the girls had had enough of the amusements, and we had provoked a few squeals by hauling them up high in the swing boats, we went to *The Lion,* During the course of the evening, I became even more puzzled by the turn of events. I found out that Heather lived some miles down the Uxbridge Road – not anywhere near her friend, Blanche. It was obvious that, if progress was to be made, they would have to split up. The girls knew this, and were apparently prepared to cope with their military escorts singly.

Eventually, after several small drinks and a walk around, the girls decided it was time to go home. We split up, and Heather and I caught a trolley bus. Heather was chatty, and good company. She talked animatedly on the bus, and she held my arm possessively. As I found out more, I discovered that she was interested in sport, and had been a junior county sprinter while at Central School. She in turn was fascinated by some of my history, as I briefly sketched it.

We got off. I took careful note of my surroundings, but I had a good idea of the neighbourhood. We turned into a large residential road, and then off again.

'I live just round the corner,' said Heather, at last. We were standing on a piece of waste ground, at the corner of two roads. It was grassy, and planted with ornamental trees and shrubs. On the opposite side of the street was a concrete surface air raid shelter, with a secluded, grassy patch behind it. The evening had been a pleasant one. Heather clearly found me an attraction, and we had proved to be mutually pleasant company. She responded readily enough when I kissed her. We came out of a little, tight clinch, and I stood facing her, wondering what the next move should be, or what she expected. We were quiet for a few minutes.

'What are you thinking about?' she asked after a while.

Impelled by the desire to make ground, and goaded by the feeling that I must make the running this time, I replied, quickly before I could allow myself time for second thoughts; 'I was thinking what I could do to you, if we went over into that long grass, behind that shelter.'

There was a short pause, and I could feel her letting go of my hand.

'Oh, dear,' she sighed. 'Now you've gone and spoiled it.' She sound more sorry than angry. She went on, rubbing salt into the wound. 'I thought we had been getting on, rather well.'

As on similar occasions, I felt some small sense of relief, mixed with sexual frustration, and quickly tried to make amends. My conscience was eased, now that I realised that I should not have to try to press her, or to seduce her, into some action that she might regret later.

I'm sorry,' I said, simply. 'I don't know what made me say that.' I paused for a moment. 'It has been a smashing evening, and I have enjoyed being with you very much.'

She thought for a minute. 'Yes, it has been fun,' she said. 'But

108

you must be disappointed that I am not the sort of girl that you and your friend were looking for.'

'No, not really,' I replied. 'I don't suppose you'll want to see me again, but I would still very much like to take you out; that is, if you'll let me start again.'

'I'd like to,' she said. 'You've only got two or three days – perhaps we could go to the flicks tomorrow.'

She had clearly dismissed my fall from grace as a minor matter – one of the hazards of going out with a soldier. I kissed her goodnight, and she responded generously.

I was just able to catch the last trolley bus to Uxbridge, and then walk. Again, my thoughts were all mixed up. I had gone out after a pick-up, and instead seemed to be getting tangled up without gaining what I was after. But she was nice!

I called on Bill on Monday afternoon. Things had gone a little differently with Blanche. She had not allowed him, I was told, very many liberties, and they had made no further arrangements. He looked at me with envy.

'You're a luck sod!' he exclaimed. 'You soon got in, there. Don't know how you do it.'

I smiled to myself. 'Bloody hell! Do what!' I thought.

I met her outside the Odeon, near to where she lived. I had decided to wear civvies. After all, I was not out to make a catch tonight.

She did look very pretty, with her long, shapely legs and trim figure. She greeted me warmly, all set to allow me a fresh start. I was a bit careful, in the cinema, and I kept off the old button routine. We went for a drink after the film, then I took her home. She invited me in, without embarrassment. I was introduced to her parents. Mrs. Cother gave me a keen glance, but she was apparently satisfied with what she saw. She had heard that, although I was a soldier, I was also a local boy, and she felt that Heather could cope. We sat on the settee alone in the sitting room, long after her parents had gone to bed, and kissed and cuddled passionately. Heather, of course, was in command of the situation, and I dared try nothing risky. I had made my play, clumsy and ill-advised as it obviously had been, and now I had to play it on her terms.

The last bus had gone, and so I walked and trotted the seven or so miles home without bother, and crept into bed.

Again, it seemed, I was an unfortunate victim of circumstance, as I found myself deeply attracted to a girl just as I was being posted. To think that I had spent all those, often bleak, months in Hounslow, and had only just met her.

The following night, we went for a drink. Farewells were tender, sad, and prolonged, as I was to be away, on Wednesday. I promised to write, and she knew that I would. Young as she was, she knew that she had me on a string, at least for the time being.

The holding unit had taken over a row of empty houses, near Chigwell. We were billeted, six or seven to a room, and regimentation was dispensed with. There was an early morning P.T. parade, and some weapon drills, with field craft, in the surrounding woods and fields, but nothing too serious. Weekends were free, but nobody was allowed to go far, as postings came through at short notice. There were still remnants of my Chester intake around, as well as a few buddies from the signals course. Bob was still there, and so was Geoff Collard. Most of the others had gone on draft to service battalions, or had been transferred to rifle regiments, many of them Scottish. I was able to get home, and I continued to meet Heather, who had temporarily deserted Blanche, to meet the demands of her new soldier boy friend. Bill Turley was back at Chester, waiting for a posting.

After two or three weeks came the weekend that I knew would be my last at Chigwell. My number had come up to join a service battalion, 'somewhere in England,' the following week. Luckily, Bob Eldridge was on the same draft.

The weekend was tender, delightful, and sad. I had arranged to meet Heather, at home, and then travel on to London Bridge, to catch my train. We were both affected by the parting. Heather seemed to be in a more pliant mood, almost daring me, with her eyes, to sweep her into a surrender. Would she yield, now that I was going away for an indefinite time? Would she be prepared to give in, in the hope that this would bring me back to her? I became aware of the change in her, and, mentally, I tried to will my hands into decisive action. But there were no loose blouse buttons that would part so obligingly, and give me a start. I gazed at her long stocking-clad legs, as I pressed her into the settee. My resolve melted, as I thought of the terrible consequences of a false move. The moment passed; she sighed, and kissed my ear gently as the tension relaxed.

I had delayed the parting as long as I dared, before running down the road to catch the bus to Shepherd's Bush. Having got to the stop, I discovered that the last bus had gone. Being Sunday, the service finished earlier, and I had forgotten this. Desperately, I set off, running and walking, to Hanwell, where I could pick up a later bus. It was quite a few miles, but I made it, and eventually caught the bus. I arrived at London Bridge station, far too late, and, resigned to trouble, I reported to the RTO's office with my weekend pass. To my surprise, the RTO on duty was an American sergeant – this was something that I had not met before.

'What d'you want, buddy?' came the question, as I stood in the office.

I showed my pass. 'I've missed the train,' I said.

'How the heck did you manage that, then, soldier?' came the breezy reply.

I told him the story – how I had lingered with my last goodbyes at my girl's house, and forgotten that the buses stopped earlier on Sundays; how I had hoofed it all the way to Hanwell to pick up a later bus, and here I was.

The American looked at me, appreciatively. In his opinion, I had got my priorities right! I had, he thought, obviously given my girl an adequate farewell, and I had been unlucky.

'I guess these janes are the cause of most of a guy's problems,' he said. He thought, for a moment. 'I'll do what I can,' he said, with a sigh. 'I just hope you make it, buddy. You sure are going to be adrift.' He thought, for a moment. 'I'll do what I can,' he said, with another sigh. Taking the pass, he wrote across the top 'Arrived, London Bridge – 1.30 hours – buses and trains from Uxbridge, delayed!' and stamped it.

I looked at the pass in amazement and gratitude.

'Thanks, very much,' I said.

'Weell, I guess you were late in a good cause,' was the reply.

I got back to the billet at 5.45, and paraded for P.T. at 7.00 hours. The sergeant was not pleased, but took no action, in view of the information on the pass. By the end of the day, however, I had had enough. I crept into bed as early as I could, absolutely whacked. I slipped down under my blankets, on the bare boards of an upstairs room, and I slept till morning.

Chapter 10

The soldiers on the draft arrived by train at their Kent coast holiday resort, at about 1600 hours. We were received, without ceremony, by a CSM, accompanied by a bevy of corporals. In twos and threes, we were detailed off to companies and platoons, and we set off to our billets. Most of the corporals and privates were quartered in two or three large empty hotels, right on the sea front. There was no furniture, and the soldiers each occupied a section of the bare wooden floor.

I found myself in 'D' company, mortars, where I was to learn how to handle the deadly weapon that had reputedly caused such havoc in the recent invasion of Sicily.

Having dumped our kit, we newcomers came down to get our bearings. It was tea time, and details were being marched through the street, to the huge amusement arcade that was now the battalion cookhouse and dining area. We had expected the regimental routine that we had become accustomed to. It was therefore a pleasant surprise to find that any corporal, having collected a group of men together, would then march them off to tea with the minimum fuss.

The following morning, who should I bump into but Bill Turley. He had recently come from Chester, and was also in 'D' company, but in another platoon. I had a chat with him one evening, and brought him up to date with the news of my romance. Bob Eldridge was also in 'D' company, in my platoon – number one – billeted on the fifth floor of a once well-known hotel.

The town of Margate was pleasant in late summer. There were no civilian visitors, and travel was restricted. However, the beach was safe and the sea warm.

Within a few days Heather, in response to my request, sent me a photo. She looked lovely, and I was able to flaunt her picture round with some pride and to the envy of my mates on the fifth floor.

The following day, number one platoon set off for the company store, on the ground floor of the hotel. The older hands fetched out the base plates and barrels of the mortars, and the simple mechanism of the monster was quickly made clear to the beginners.

In the afternoon, a mortar was set up on the beach, pointing out to sea, and the platoon stood by while a corporal took a bomb and poked it down the mouth of the long barrel. The bomb slid to the bottom, where it struck the firing pin, and was launched out to sea. The bang of the thing, when it went off, was much louder than I had expected, and a number of us were visibly startled. The corporal then slid nine more bombs down the barrel, and the ten missiles were air-borne, before the first one hit the sea, some two thousand yards away, making a tremendous water spout. The others exploded, in succession, making an awesome spectacle each time.

The next two or three weeks were gruelling ones, with mortar drills and further infantry training. The soldiers in the machine gun companies and the mortar company had to complete their basic infantry tests, including rifle proficiency and the physical standards.

The first of the physical tests took place one afternoon when the platoon was mustered for the 'ten mile bash'. This was a standard test, in which the platoon, as a unit, marched and double along ten miles of road. The time limit to complete the course was two hours. Number one platoon completed this without much trouble, although battle order was worn and rifles were carried. The following day, each soldier had to complete two miles across country, in boots and denims and wearing a helmet, in eighteen minutes.

As the battalion got into the swing of things, the daily routine was drastically adjusted to suit combat conditions. Breakfast was taken at 1900 hours, and the 'day' then proceeded – all through the night! If we were lucky, we would finish at 0800 hours.

One night, we set off in trucks, and travelled inland. After an hour, we de-bussed and lugged our heavy weapons across country for three miles. The emphasis was on speed and silence; some of the things said by the sweating mortar carriers were ex-dictionary. At the end of the journey, we had a short rest, and then we were set to climb camouflaged assault rigging hanging over a quarry face. It was here that the battalion suffered its first casualty. Our popular company second in command, Captain Whylie, fell backwards at the top of the rigging, to a distance of fifteen feet. He suffered a back injury and left the battalion, never to return.

Bob remained a close pal. He had a girl friend back home, whom he had met before he had joined up. She had contracted T.B. and was in a sanatorium in Surrey. Bob visited her when he could. He spoke of her often and was obviously very attached to her. however, this did not inhibit him unduly in his social life, and he had successfully completed a number of operations involving ladies of the town. Bob was a cheerful, gregarious and kind-hearted chap, and, with a few pals, we had some good nights in the town taverns. Sometimes, I found myself at a loose end on the evenings when my mates had assignations with the girls. I had thoughts only for one girl at a time, and I would spend such an evening writing long, sentimental letters to Heather.

In August, the battalion migrated to mid-Wales. Here, we were to undergo manoeuvres involving other units, and we were to fire our weapons on designated areas of moorland. Local farmers had been notified of the danger areas of moorland, so that livestock could be safeguarded, but it was impossible for the sheep farmers to round up the scattered flocks, and they were compensated for any animals 'killed in action'.

My company started this operation as riflemen. This meant that we advanced under covering fire from the MMG's. The MMG company set off on the first morning. The battalion had spent the night in halls and deserted schools, in Rhayader and Llandrindod Wells. The infantry were transported to their starting line in TCVs, and then force-marched, for three miles. Already, the steady rattle of MMG fire could be heard, interspersed with the awful crump of mortar fire. The mortars had laid down a smoke screen on the lower slopes of the hill which was to be assaulted. The riflemen took cover, keeping their heads low, knowing that the machine gunners would be firing on fixed lines, over their heads. As I lay, face down amid the bracken, the flies pestered me in swarms, attracted by the sweat and grime. The bullets from the machine guns were sending up little spouts ahead.

'Bloody 'ell!' exclaimed Bob, gasping for breath, 'I only hope those bleeders set their sights right! I don't want a round of 303 up my arse!' This was a sentiment that was echoed by all of us.

The smoke thickened up in front of the target. Studying his watch, and listening carefully to his wireless link, Lieutenant Kenny blew his whistle for the advance. As we stood, hoping the machine gun support fire was lifting on time, the crumps of mortar seemed too close for comfort. We charged through the smoke, and made up the hill, sobbing for breath, and choking from the acrid fumes. Lying down forward of the 'captured' positions, we were 'screamed' into action, as we came under fire from a gun on our right. This was too close for comfort, and we knew that the fire was to be switched to our positions within two or three minutes, so we needed little urging to set off again.

When the action was over, Bob and I went with some others of the platoon, to see the damage wrought by one mortar bomb. There had been three scraggy, hill steers in a small upland pasture in the line of fire – one, more or less, in each corner of the field. For some reason, they had not been moved.

'Probably worth more dead, in compensation,' said the platoon sergeant.

They were all three dead, but with little sign of injury on their bodies.

'Burst their bloody lungs,' said a corporal, an old soldier of the platoon.

Again that night, we slept in Rhayader.

The following day there was a mortar exercise. The target was at the foot of a hill – range of about three thousand-five hundred yards. The mortars were 'humped' into position after their Lloyd carrier transporters had brought them up. They were then set down below a crest, our of view of the target. Number one platoon was serving two mortars. Bob had a soft job in the observation post, ahead and to the right. The officer in the OP would wireless back directions for the adjustment of the line and the elevation. There were a lot of bombs fired that morning, and the troops were glad to rest at midday, and eat the hot stew brought up from the rear. We had carried a lot of heavy bomb cases up the trail by then.

We were allowed to rest in the afternoon, and we were then briefed for a map and compass exercise across the moors, to last all night. At 0600 hours next morning, we lay on our faces like idiots, ready to made a final assault, before breakfast. Then we slept through the morning, and set off at midday to new positions. Here we dug slit trenches, set up ground sheets as 'bivvies', and spent a wet night out on the moors. We 'stood to' at dawn, just to round off the week.

Back at Margate, routine training went ahead. The manoeuvres became progressively more extensive, involving other units of our division, and, on occasion, Americans as well.

We were becoming a seasoned, welded unit, fitting smoothly, into our role with brigade and division. Leave was now non-existent.

Again, I had a stroke of luck when, just before the trip to Wales, Charlie Salt, the secretary of my old running club, had sent a request for me to run in an event at Windsor. The C.O. granted a weekend pass. Such events were encouraged, so as to give maximum support to the 'holidays at home' campaign floated by the government. I duly ran in a three mile event, with no outstanding success, and had the rest of the Saturday and Sunday at home. I had had to show my pass on several occasions to M.P.s, in and around Victoria, as leave from my unit on the south-east coast was known to be rare. Also, I was clearly labelled with regimental flash and divisional emblem, and the deployment of the Second Army was well known to those whose business it was to know.

I spent Saturday evening with Heather at her home, where we were alone in the house. Again we kissed and cuddled, as skillfully as I knew how. I had made some progress in this department, and she stretched out on the settee, apparently in an attitude of relaxed acquiescence. She had smiled at me in a way that had made me wonder whether she considered the preliminaries were over, and I was left wondering whether she expected me to make another bid. After one period of silence, and in a moment of courage, I had put my hand firmly on the front of her thigh, under her neatly arranged skirt. She had stiffened and kept very still and quiet, either waiting for what was to follow, or showing an as yet unspoken disapproval. In any event, my courage failed, and the weekend passed without more action.

The battalion continued to practise its role as support for the infantry rifle battalions of the division, and exercises continued to be extensive and prolonged.

There had been some shuffling of personnel, as a result of which a number of trained soldiers from the other three support regiments joined us, to replace an equal number who were posted out, mainly to the RNFs and the Cheshires. Army policy was to mix up units in this way, so that any subsequent heavy casualties did not fall too heavily on any one town. Also, many of the battalion were older men, who had already seen action in France and Belgium in 1940, or in the Middle East. They were the stiffening that would see we younger men through our baptism of fire. The relationships between officers, N.C.O.s and men, were generally very good. Everyone did his job, and regimentation and 'bull' were at the minimum. The N.C.O.s especially knew that these were the men that they were going to have to go to war with – the men whom their own lives might one day depend on. I had noticed the difference as soon as I had arrived in this battalion, and I felt more at ease.

War or no war, some things could not be shelved, and one such was the divisional boxing championships, in which unit met unit on a 'knock out' basis. Each battalion or battery fielded a team of nine boxers, at the various weights. To this battalion, which had already won the the championship for the last two years, it was an event almost to rival Hitler's war.

There were vacancies in the battalion team due to postings and injuries, and the colonel ordered the P.T. staff to find replacements. This was done simply by organising inter-platoon and inter-company contests.

I had done a little boxing in the club at school, and I had had to learn to 'rough it' as a boy, when my father had coached me on the lawn to 'look after myself'. With this background, and a long reach, I found myself progressing through the lists, at platoon and company level.

I had been bustled into a bloody encounter, at platoon level, almost without being aware of what was going on. In this bout, I had been matched with a lance-corporal of considerable experience – a rough, extrovert Cockney. When the draw had been made, my opponent, Lance-Corporal McNab, said to me, in the hearing of his mates, 'Cor, 'aint I lucky to have drawn you.' Whether this was meant to be pre-fight nerve jangling, or whether he genuinely thought of me as a soft option, I don't know. In any event, the little incident was just what was needed to make me hard enough and mean enough to spark off my aggression.

The resulting contest was a three round firework display, in which we two contestants exploded in the centre of the ring, and spilled a considerable quantity of blood. I won, on points – progressed to represent company, and made a firm and lasting friend of Lance-Corporal McNab.

The ultimate result of these skirmishes was that I was billed to represent the battalion, and thus I became embroiled with a rugged rural boy from the Dorsets. I won this one, by judicious use of a straight left, and a bit of 'toe' to 'toe'. This helped the battalion through to the next round, against an artillery unit. Again there was success all round.

The semi-final, against the Wiltshires, was a particularly bloody battle.

The 'Moonrakers' had a common, unorthodox style, difficult to combat. As I sat below the ring, waiting to climb in for my bout, which was next, I felt the nerves of my stomach knotting, as they always did at this stage of a contest.

'You bloody idiot!' I told myself, wishing I could be anywhere else but where I was; 'how do you manage to get yourself in this bloody silly situation, again and again!'

I felt happier, once I was sitting in my corner, with my gloved arms stretching along the ropes. There were a few whispered words from my second as the bell went. We circled each other warily before my opponent surged in, bringing his right hand up, from about the level of his knee in a bone-crunching swing. This had been the style in previous bouts, so I was not unprepared, and I was able to duck forward, allowing the blow to scrape over my head. At the same time, I got in a straight left jab at my opponent's already bent nose. Then I danced out of range. I continued, like this, for the rest of the round.

'For Christ's sake, George, watch that 'bolo' swing,' said Corporal Bate, my second; 'I think you shaded that round, but he's bloody dangerous!'

We came out for the second round, and the Wiltshire lad instantly swung over a 'sucker' punch. I saw flashes of light as the blow, only partially parried, caught me on the bridge of the nose. The pain was excrutiating. Dancing out of range and covering up, I waited for my head to clear. My opponent came in, both hands swinging wildly, and I had difficulty in keeping him out. As it was, I caught a second swing, on the side of the jaw, and I felt a sharp pain, below my right ear, where my lower jaw was hinged. I was glad to hear the bell.

'Don't let him catch you again, George, with one of those

swings,' said Corporal Bate; 'you'll 'ave ter win the last round. Keep yer distance, an' use yer reach.'

The pain in my nose was now a dull ache, but it soon started to bleed again, making breathing difficult. My opponent was still strong, but he got careless and suffered the penalty. In charging forward for another mighty swing, he lowered his left. I stepped in with a solid right, and followed this with a left uppercut. My opponent kept going, and he stayed dangerous, but those two blows, coming as they did in the final round, slowed him up to a point where he became vulnerable. He stopped a few more left jabs before the bell went, and I had won on points. The battalion went on to win that match by a narrow margin, and so reached the final.

My nose was broken. It was nothing very serious but it was very tender. The MC assured me that I would be alright for the final, against the Hampshires.

'I dunno what you do it for,' said Bob. 'This job's rough enough wivout you getting yerself bashed up fer nuffin' ''

'He was wrong about the 'nuffin'. The first 'perk' was that I was left behind, on a rear party with the other boxers, when the battalion went off on a particularly nasty night carry, followed by a climb up assault netting and over a cliff face, carrying guns. While this was going on, my nose mended and was as good as new, apart from a slight kink.

After the reshuffle between the support regiments, I was asked, as were many of the others, if I would like to stay in the mortar company, or would I prefer to go to one of the machine gun companies, where my previous training would be welcomed. We were interviewed by our platoon officer, Lieutenant Kenny. Bob and I opted for the Vickers, and duly transferred to another hotel. For the next week or two we brushed up on our machine gunnery until we became as quick and as automatic in reaction as in our Chester days. We also learnt how to operate the larger wireless sets used in the bren carriers. As well as all this, I was still involved in the boxing, and I had to attend strict training routines in the drill hall, and I kept off the drink. I was also allowed early nights, and no guard duties. Yes, war was war, but the boxing championships were, as usual with the Diehards, a top priority!

I suppose we were pretty well at the peak of fitness when the final of the divisional championships drew near. The final was a big affair, and took place in a splendid hall on the Sussex coast at Bexhill. The division was deployed all around this area, and the hall was filled to capacity. The crowd arrangements were in the hands of the military police.

There is little to say. Our battalion won the final by the narrowist of margins. I managed to win what was considered to be a skillful bout, on points, and the presentations were made by our famous Second Army commander himself. The victorious team members were granted five days leave and soon departed to the station, to the envy of the rest of the battalion.

I went home, wondering how things were going to go with Heather. She had sometimes hinted at an older, civilian admirer, and it had become evident of late, that she had been meeting him quite often. I had become increasingly irritated by more frequent allusions to him; I knew that he was pressing, and that he knew about my existence. As a consequence, our meetings during the next few days of this bonus leave were vaguely niggling. I did not know what I should do. When I was on my own, I tried to imagine the outcome of any 'strong arm' tactics I might try. I had even thought that the time might be right to overcome her initial protests one night, and simply get on with it and 'lay' her on the soft sitting room carpet. However, when I was with her I was at a loss – indecisive – and our meetings broke up with increasing frustration – certainly on my part. I was being played along, and it was become increasingly evident that there was no lasting promise in our relationship. The thought of getting her on that carpet was almost more than flesh and blood could stand!

On the last day of the short leave, I decided to play it straight, and tell her that she must choose between me and her older civvy boy friend, who admittedly had known her a lot longer than I had. I was not going to play second fiddle any longer. Rather to my surprise, I discovered that I didn't feel unduly bothered about the possible outcome of my 'ultimatum'. I stuck to my guns, and was able to sustain a very hard line when we were alone in the sitting room. She was surprised, and little upset. I think she thought that she still had me on a piece of string. Anyway, she begged me not to make an issue of it just yet, but I had gone too far to pull back. It was a pleasant feeling to be 'in the saddle' and to hear her begging me not to ask her to make an impossible decision. She still hoped to string us both along. Keeping my resolve and my temper, I ended up by telling her that I would not see her on my next leave. I reckoned afterwards that that was the time I could have made her come across, but I returned to Margate, almost relieved to be back!

Several of the more promising younger members of the battalion had been on an instruction cadre, and some of us were picked for continuation courses, provided by our company commanders. I found this interesting, and, of course, there were promotion prospects in the wind. We learnt some valuable map work, as well as the finer art of the positioning and the setting of the guns. We learnt how to calculate the trajectory or curve of the bullets in flight, and so how to site the weapons so that we could fire on unseen targets. The whole thing seemed a bit like surveying. At the end of the course, a number of us were promoted to lance corporal, with a view to early promotion to full corporal. Thus, I, George Milton, became an NCO in the King's Army.

At about this time, the new rifles came – and they really were new. The old SMLE, that had done such sterling work, had now been relegated to a training weapon. The new rifles came in cardboard boxes, packed solid with grease. Each man below full corporal was given his box. It was with a certain feeling of awe, that I extricated my rifle from the cocoon of thick grease, and set about cleaning it, ready for the inevitable thorough inspection. The number of the rifle was entered in the log, and each soldier duly signed. From now on, this was it – the rifle that would have to see me through whatever was to come. Within two or three days, all the troops had been bussed out to the ranges to fire them and have the sights adjusted on the spot by an armourer. Each gun was adjusted to suit the style of its new owner, and from then on the pair were to become almost inseparable.

As a lance-jack, my routine changed in certain respects. I was now expected to march squads to and from the cookhouse; I sat at the end of a table and served the food; I posted pickets, and I was responsible for the general order of a section of the billet.

Enemy planes had been active at night, attacking nearby Manston aerodrome, although the RAF had quit it long before. Some of the nights were distinctly noisy, but little real damage was done. The enemy could have done themselves more good by bombing the coastal hotels, where their prospective invaders were present.

To combat low level invaders, mostly Focke-Wulfs, the battalion had a number of twin Vickers, mounted on the back of fifteen-hundred weight trucks, along the shore line. These were manned by a corporal and four men, for a twenty-four hour shift. Their chances of bothering an enemy pilot were considered small.

One morning, my team was just handing over to a new one, which had a full corporal in charge. Our watch had been without incident, as had been expected. The ammunition was checked, and the new corporal sat in the seat in the back of the truck, behind his guns, mainly to check that everything was just as he would want it in the unlikely event of his being called on to shoot in anger. It was early in the morning. I was keen to get my men off to breakfast. The new NCO, Corporal McMann, was a dour, experienced soldier, who had been in the Middle East, and who had been transferred from the RNFs in the recent reshuffle. He had checked the belt and was peering at the ring sight, between the guns, with his thumbs on the common firing button. At that very moment, when the team was at its most alert, a German pilot brought his Focke-Wulf sweeping in from the sea, low and fast.

Corporal McMann saw him in his sights, and automatically

120

swivelled his guns as he sent about 1000 rounds per minute from twin barrels winging towards the target. My crew had taken cover by the side of the truck, from where we could see the tracer bullets, which were distributed along the ammunition belt, for sighting purposes, apparently pumping into the belly of the plane. The Focke-Wulf veered crazily and plunged into the sea, close inshore. It did not explode, probably because of the water. The noise quickly brought more men, pouring out of the nearby buildings. A cordon was quickly organised by the CSM of 'B' company, to keep any civilian sightseers away.

The whole battalion was cock-a-hoop. It was 'one in the eye' for the light ack ack boys, just down the coast. The corporal and I each made our required statements. The later news was even more astounding. The luckless pilot had been carrying more information, in the form of marked maps and documents, than he should. As a consequence, RAF intelligence were able to piece together valuable information about his base and flight plan.

There were no more adventures of this kind. Shortly after, news filtered through that the battalion was moving down the coast, to quarters near Folkstone.

Chapter Eleven

The move to the south east coast was in convoy. The battalion was assembled after breakfast, and, platoon by platoon, boarded their transport which was mustered along the coast road. Most of the gun teams travelled in their bren carriers, with the Lloyd carriers following the brens, and the trucks following them with more troops, stores, HQ staff and ammunition. The RSM's truck, carrying a red flag, brought up the rear. The whole convoy travelled at a steady speed, but as usual the vehicles at the back always seemed to be travelling faster than those at the front. Dispatch riders, on their Matchless motorbikes, sped up and down the line of vehicles and held up the traffic at all crossroads and junctions. The good citizens of Kent and Sussex were well accustomed to troop movements, but such columns, moving southwards, always occasioned special interest and speculation.

On the outskirts of Folkestone, the company divided, with DRs directing each company to its destination. 'A' company duly arrived at a convent, where they were to be billeted – the nuns having left. This was a good billet in many ways, with solid walls and ceilings. The men slept in large rooms with bunk beds.

One town was very much like another. Those who were first to get out for a look round were able to report on the pubs, cinemas, dance halls and transport facilities. The additional excitement that Folkestone had to offer was the occasional shell lobbed at us from across the Channel.

There was an increasing feeling of imminent happenings as the weeks went on. This was heightened by a number of events.

The first of these was the buzz that went round that the division was to be 'mobilised'. Like most of the other younger ones, I wasn't too sure what that meant. I was soon to find out. It was a case of 'clear the decks for action'. We all had a medical check. All those who were not A1 were promptly transferred out of the unit. All those with flat feet and 'gammy' knees had to go. All kit was carefully checked and replacements were made, on a more generous basis than usual. Everyone was given an extra course of immunisation – in some cases for diseases not before mentioned, like typhus and blackwater fever. Mail was censored. There was no leave. From now on, we were ready for anything.

The second event left us in no doubt, if there had been any doubts left to have. There was news of a big parade in the offing, and we were all set to the task of preparing for an important occasion. Battalions assembled in TCVs and trucks, and motored out to the South Downs, where an unusually large review was to take place.

We of 'A' company, who were the first to arrive, soon realised that something big was afoot. Already, there were other battalions assembled, and it became evident that most of the division was on parade. The battalions were marshalled, and rapidly inspected for general correctness. The dress was boots, belts, webbing gaiters and belts. Rifles were carried. The beret had replaced the forage cap as general headwear some time before.

The parade was brought to attention, battalion by battalion, when a staff car appeared, bearing a flag on the bonnet. The figure who emerged, with his black beret and khaki pullover, was unmistakable.

The great man spoke briefly to the senior officers of the battalions as he walked quickly round. He happened to choose the support battalion for his more detailed inspection. He strode between the extended ranks, platoon by platoon, and company by company. As he came round the end of the rank, where I was, he glanced piercingly at me, paused, and then stopped. I froze, wondering what the hell had gone wrong with my bearing that was going to make serious trouble.

'I think we've met before, young man,' he said, after a pause.

'Yes, sir,' I replied.

'Yes, if I'm not mistaken, it was the evening of a lively boxing match,' he went on.

'Yes, sir,' I said, again.

'I hope you are going to be as useful with the machine gun,' he said, cryptically.

'Yes, sir,' I said, yet again.

At first, I was amazed and very impressed by the great man's eye for detail, but long afterwards I came to the conclusion that he had 'done his homework'. Even so, I remained impressed.

Standing on a dais, the general called upon the troops to 'gather round'. We broke ranks, in an orderly fashion of course, and drew closer. He addressed us, using a megaphone.

'. . . you are some of the men who have been chosen . . . first assault corps . . . Europe . . . fit for the task . . . making history. . .'

'Muck our luck, then!' came a voice down the rank.

Well, we had all known, more or less anyway, but now there was little doubt. So that was it!

He got back into his staff car and was swept away, no doubt to break the news to some other lucky division. I felt something: perhaps even a strange elation. I knew we weren't quite good enough yet, but the months and years of conditioning were going to be tested before so very long.

Little was said in the TCVs and the trucks as we were driven back to Folkestone. What was there to say!

The bren gun carrier was the common form of transport in the machine gun platoons – there were about eight of them in each platoon, and it was necessary that there should be as many men as possible able to drive them. It wouldn't do to be stranded because the recognised driver became a casualty.

I was therefore in one of the several groups to be set to work, in the autumn, learning to master this sometimes very temperamental vehicle.

I started the course by being shown the controls by my instructor, who then promptly set me in the driving seat, and we were off, through Sandgate. The carrier behaved well, provided that the clutch was used very carefully. Any poor control of clutch or gears would send the front of the thing bumping up and down on the road, to the discomfort of the crew. It was a track-laying vehicle, and it had a special steering feature, in that changes of direction, of a few degrees, were effected by a 'bowing' of the tracks. In unskilled, or unlucky hands, it could be a harzardous monster. A broken track could whip up over the top, to the danger of the crew perched in the back. It could skid on a metalled road, and not turn as required. It could turn over, if driven carelessly on sloping ground, and put the crew in grave peril; but it was fast, manoeuvrable, and ideal for the quick loading and unloading of guns and crews.

One Saturday morning, six of these 'armoured boxes' were bowling along the road, on driving instruction. I was in the second one, sitting at the back. The road swept right. Unfortunately, the leading vehicle, with a learner-private at the wheel, went straight on, on locked tracks – straight into a concrete tank block. The block was designed to stop a tank, and it certainly stopped the carrier. The whole crew were shaken up, but the luckless driver banged his face on the steel plate in front of him, and smashed his face to a horrifying and messy degree. The rest stopped, and my team made the poor chap as comfortable as possible. Fortunately, a passing vehicle with plenty of room, stopped. The casualty was laid out, and driven to hospital.

"'E'll get a bloody shock, if 'e wakes up afore 'e gets to dock,' said Ginger Ames. "'E'll fink 'e's 'ad 'is chips.'

Ginger's sentiments were understandable – the makeshift ambulance was an empty hearse!

During the next few weeks, long hours were spent in mastering the carrier. As well as driving, this involved long, cold mornings carrying out the 'daily tasks' of vehicle maintenance. One of the worst jobs, I found, was handling the heavy track links, or messing about with the driving wheels or bogies. However, I became quite proficient at the wheel, and drove, during some intensive exercises, along the metalled roads and across the downland. It is true that I did 'nudge' a delivery van parked in Lewes High Street, but on the whole, I became quite useful. The really good drivers could work wonders, and 'screamed' their vehicles up hair-raising slopes, round hairpin bends, and along the frightening drops and cliff hangers. Many of the exercises were carried out around Lewes, with the troops sleeping in barns and straw ricks, or just on the ground alongside their vehicles.

All in all, these exercises were not arduous – not in the way that the extended exercises in Wales had been. They were largely movement exercises, testing the mobility and deployment of large numbers of vehicles and supplies.

During the boxing tournament, I had become more widely known, and I was in consequence readily absorbed into a wider drinking circle than ever. As well as this, there were dances in the Leas Cliff Hall, and there was the cinema.

Although Bob Eldridge was now an established wireless operator in HQ company, we were still fast buddies. On several occasions I had made a foursome when Bob had teamed up with a local lady, but no really passionate interludes had developed from these encounters. The battalion had been in Folkestone for some time and would surely move soon. Units were being switched round in a kaleidoscopic fashion, even on occasion swapping billeting areas or camps with the Americans. The purpose of all this movement was beyond the comprehension of mere soldiers.

The social patterns and relationships between soldiers and civilians was interesting. The younger soldiers, still in their teens or early twenties, stepped out in the town, hoping to make fleeting conquests among the girls who frequented the pubs and dances, usually in groups of two or three. I fell into this category, and had taken part in several skirmishes in quiet corners with town girls. There were lurid accounts of battes won and lost, to be heard in the convent billet, or the bars, but the sources weren't always reliable and the stories often exaggerated. Also, the onset of a hard winter inhibited these operations.

The tactics of the older soldiers, with a greater experience of romantic as well as military operations, was quite different. They sought out the women, lonely or bored, of wider experience, and 'got their feet under the table'. Many of the married men, missing the home comforts that they had known, sought out kindred spirits among the lonely wives of men abroad, the young widows or the service women who lived in accessible lodgings out of camp. Those concerned, soldiers and civilians, knew the desperate loneliness and the nagging pain of separation. In some cases, the married women were separated from overseas husbands whom they had hardly known, and these sought solace from the uncertainty of the times in the arms of a married soldier, similarly lonely. Such infidelity was fairly common in the battalion; those concerned made what they could of the situation they were in, and moved on, when the time came, usually without heartbreak on either side. Only a minority of these liaisons precipitated marital disasters, and probably less trouble was caused, to both parties, than by the 'one night stands' of the younger men with the 'enthusiastic amateurs', or with the starry-eyed girls losing their innocence in a spirit of adventure of curiosity. A strange young man from a far away place – a fit, bold young man, with uniform emblazoned with the panoply of war – divisional signs, infantry designation, and colours, badges of rank – was an attraction and a mystery.

The mystery that is woman was one that many of the young soilders hadn't even begun to solve. The success of the older and wiser men seemed to make the fever of sexual desire more frustrating and their loneliness more intense.

Such problems were not discussed very much – the young men wouldn't know how to discuss them, or who to discuss them with. The only talk was the comparing of notes about which girls were easy, or which ones 'would' with the right sought of persuasion or persistence. One or two inevitably fell victims to VD, and were temporarily, or in some cases permanently, withdrawn.

I continued to grow into my new role as junior NCO, and expected soon to get my second tape, as my training, and duties with the platoon now warranted this.

One morning, I was presented with my first 'personal' problem, by Jimmy Jukes, a serious young North Londoner whose manner was stolid and humourless.

'Can I 'ave a word wiv yer, Corp?' he asked one evening, when I was busy cleaning up and writing home.

'Sure, Jimmy, sit down,' I said, making room on my bed.

Jimmy sat down, and presented his problem.

'It's like this, Corp,' he commenced; 'I've bin gettin' worried at nights. I go to bed, an' I've bin pullin' it, quite a lot – can't stop meself, I bin doing it most nights, an' I bin gettin' worried, like.'

He looked at me sideways, apparently hoping for some curative words of wisdom. Initially, I had been quite taken aback by the nature of the problem, and my immediate reaction was to make light of it, but a look at Jimmy's earnest face made me change my mind. There was no humour in Jimmy. Obviously, he had been brought up to believe that he had developed into a wicked boy, and that something terrible was about to happen.

The problem, of course, was a common one among fit and unattached young soldiers. Most of the coarse jokes of the barrack blocks were centred around this matter of the rising sap of manhood.

'It's really only natural, Jimmy,' I said at length. 'It happens to a lot of us, an' I don't know what the answer is.' (I certainly couldn't think of an answer that would suit Jimmy.)

'Well, Corp, it ain't right,' he persisted. 'I was thinking I ought to see the MO about it.'

'Yeah; OK, Jimmy,' I agreed. 'Perhaps that's a good idea.' This was a new angle on an old problem, and I thought for a moment. Obviously, something would have to be done about Jimmy, but it didn't seem right for him to go sick. It would be the last straw, I thought, smiling to myself, if he got M and D, in bloody red ink. What would the MO say, anyway?

'Tell you what, Jimmy,' I said, after some thought. 'Let me finish this letter, an' I'll help you write to the doc', for a private talk – he'll do that for you – he's not a bad bloke.'

'Thanks, Corp,' said young Jimmy, plainly relieved at the offer. I helped him to write a simple request for advice on a personal matter. I expected that the MO would assume that poor old Jimmy had got a 'dose', and I smiled again at the very idea.

As expected, Jimmy was given an early appointment, next day. What with the transport tasks and a weapon check, I didn't see the lad, until we got back to tea, after 5.30.

'I saw the doc', Corp,' said Jimmy.

'Oh, yeah; what did he say?' I asked, wondering what to expect.

Jimmy looked at me, his long, earnest face reflecting his look of satisfied accomplishment.

'Well, 'e told me ter cut darn on the porridge fer breakfast, an' not ter 'ave a big supper in the NAAFI,' he said. 'Oh, yeah; an' 'e give me some medcin',' he added, producing a bottle of a pale orange mixture.

Although my medical knowledge was limited, I was not convinced that the MO had found the answer to Jimmy's problem.

In any event, Jimmy's mind was taken off his personal problems later that week when he spent one whole night on a driving exercise, and another on the MT picket on the beach. This duty was one not to be taken lightly. There had been some snow and the night air was bitterly cold. The guard duty involved patrolling the battalion transport, which was lined up under the face of the cliff, and well above the tide line. The usual two hours on and four off was the order, and the guards patrolled in pairs. Two hours can seem like a life time when it is spent on a very cold guard duty on a dark night.

As the winter progressed, the winds became more biting and the frost more sharp. The snow had given way to cold, clear nights, and 'A' company were grateful for their solid heated convent – so much more comfortable than the quarters of most of the battalion. Nightly jaunts were limited to the cinema or the pub. The latter places were very crowded focal points for soldiers and civilians alike. There were some noisy evenings that winter, with crowds of drinkers singing their maudlin songs, usually to the accompanyment of a battered upright piano. The Londoners usually carried the day, with *Knees up, Mother Brown, Down at the Old Bull and Bush,* and the most maudlin of all, *Nellie Dean,* the chorus of which would tail off, in a long, raucous wail. The Geordies replied with *Bladon Races,* as always. There were very few fights. There was nothing to prove, and there would be enough trouble before long. Complete strangers became bosom pals in the space of a few pints.

I sat with Bob one night at a table in the pub, with Corporal Tom Brown, a Dunkirk veteran. Tom had been drinking steadily, but instead of drowning his sorrows, he was becoming more morbid and introspective with each drink. The evening was well advanced, and the three of us had dug into a corner round a small table. I had just put down my pint, and I glanced across the table. To my astonishment and discomfort, I saw Tom weeping quietly, with the tears running down his face. His eyes had a far-away look, and when he spoke, it was half to himself.

'I tell yer, it was bloody 'orrible,' he said, with embarrassing sobs. 'I was be'ind the MG, an' we was firing over open sights. The rifle companies had retired through us, an' the Jerries appeared. We 'ad ter 'old them up.' He faltered, and then continued, 'I just kep' firin', an' they fell down, at the edge of a piece of open ground.' He paused again, and the tears welled out of his staring, blank eyes. More Jerries came on, an' we shot 'em – an' they kept coming on – an' we killed dozens and dozens – all bloody ord'nary blokes.'

He buried his head in his folded arms, and sobbed. I was stunned. So this was how fighting had affected this man – four years afterwards – he still couldn't shake off the feeling of guilt; a feeling that would perhaps never completely leave him as long as he lived. Was he to be haunted by dead Germans for the rest of his life?

'Careless talk' was another bugbear. The men had been well conditioned in security, by lectures and by such films as *The Next of Kin.* Even after a drink, most soldiers would guard their tongues, and if not, they would soon be silenced by mates, or picked up by military of civilian police.

As the bitter winter relented, the underlying tension tightened a few more notches, as further preparations became evident. The drivers of all the vehicles were instructed, and then they were put to work to 'waterproof' the transport, so that it would not fail them, if and when it was driven through water on to an alien shore.

There was one uncomfortable incident in 'B' company, billeted

128

in a four storey hotel. One Saturday morning, a group from number 3 platoon were cleaning up, when there was an almighty 'Crack' from upstairs, and bits of plaster fell from the ceiling. Immediately, there was a loud scream and a lot of shouting. The news quickly spread round the battalion that a private had 'cracked' and shot off a couple of his toes with his rifle. Little more was heard of the incident, and it certainly had no effect on morale. The luckless private disappeared from the scene. He would be court-martialled, but no doubt he thought that a live coward was better than a dead hero.

It was about this time that we started our crash introduction to the language of the enemy. One evening, the NCOs of 'A' company were assembled in the hall of the convent, where we were greeted by the company commander, Major Keene. He quickly made the reason for the parade obvious.

'I can't turn you into a bunch of linguists overnight, but were going to go over a few phrases of German. These, you will have to learn off, parrot fashion, in case you need information from the natives, in a hurry.'

This, indeed, was a change of routine. As it turned out, the phrases were not very exciting ones. One of the sergeants thought, 'what are you doing, tonight?' might have been useful, but the officer wasn't amused, and we were served up such phrases as *'Gibt es Minen oder Fallen'*, (Are there any mines or booby traps) and *'Guten Tag, Guten Morgen,'* and *'Guten Abend'.*

'In between these brain shaking sessions, I was spending my spare time drinking with various mates from the company. Bob, my old mate from 70th Battalion days, was still around in HQ company, and we often spent an evening or a Saturday afternoon round the town or in the pub. Bob was still very attached to his girl in hospital, and he was able to see her fairly often, as she was in Surrey; but his was the nature that demanded female company, and he was, to use his words, a 'home and away' boy. Probably, he didn't really deceive his regular girl when he became temporarily, involved with a local lass, because there can be little doubt that she knew her Bob well enough, and accepted him for what he was. He was, after all, very loyal to her in that he always came back.

He was a shrewd lad. In spite of his cheerful and generous nature, he had grown up in a hard world, different in so many ways from mine. We both knew this, but we made a good team – that is, except where ladies were concerned. I was not the ideal partner to make up a foursome; at least, not for more than one meeting. I didn't make enough progress, quickly enough, to give Bob time to hook his own fish securely. Consequently, I found myself at a loose end, wandering the town from pub to pub, and from group to group, trying to drown my sense of loneliness and desolation, which was strong even among such close comrades: all this, while Bob was out courting some desirable lady.

One Saturday, Bob invited me to join him for a quiet day with friends, along the coast, at Hythe. With nothing better to do, and not knowing anything about the arrangements, I agreed.

We set off at midday, got a lift in a 15 cwt truck, and dropped off at the edge of the town. It was evident that some sort of carnival was planned, as there were flags and streamers festooning the lampposts. We discovered that there was to be a May Day parade, with a procession and jollifications. Bob had made the acquaintance of a young lady, Anne, who lived on the outskirts of the town. Anne was a Londoner – in fact, her old home was not far from where Bob had lived – and she and her mother had been bombed out in 1940. They had moved out of London and had been allocated a two bedroomed maisonette, just on the edge of town. Bob had met her at a Saturday dance, when she and her mother had bussed out for the evening. I had been involved with the boxing at the time, and drinking and late nights had been out.

Anne was young; seventeen or eighteen, I guessed. I gathered from Bob that she was not an easy girl to date, as she mostly travelled around with Lil, her mother, and this did tend to cramp the style of the lads. Trust Bob! He had been patient and tactful from the start, and he took them both out for a drink on most visits. Not that Lil was really a 'guardian angel' mum – but she was a mum! She was an out-going, fair-haired woman, in her middle or late thirties, sturdy, without being plump, and well-preserved. There appeared to be no man in her life. Her husband had either died, or gone away, some years ago, and she seemed as though she was content. She and Anne both worked, and there appeared to be no financial problems. As far as she was concerned, her daughter was a working girl who should be able to run her own life, and she liked Bob, although she did not regard him as an angel.

Bob had arranged to meet them at the recreation ground, where the carnival procession was to start and finish. There had been some relaxation of late, and such assemblies were now considered to be reasonably safe. In any event, there were spotters around the coast, and there would be sufficient warning of any enemy aircraft to enable the crowds to take quick cover.

The parade was the culmination of a 'Wings for Victory' week. There was an expectancy all along the south coast that the 'Balloon would go up' shortly, and we young soldiers, who were becoming part of the furniture, would be in the thick of it. It was the mothers among the local inhabitants who found the most heartache when they looked at we boisterous, young, lusty sons of other mothers. To them, we were boys – not the men that most had become, and others would become very quickly.

130

The procession having formed up, set off through the centre of the town, led by a squadron of ATC and their band, followed by Scouts, Guides, St. John's Ambulance Brigade, and the Home Guard. The Army had managed a couple of scout cars and a Matilda, and there were a few moderately decorated floats.

As the procession proceeded along the street, Girl Guides went among the onlookers with their 'Buy a Spitfire' collecting boxes.

After the circuit round the streets, there was the judging of fancy dress, and kiddies' races.

About six o'clock we called in at a café and treated ourselves to a reasonable tea. I was in a contented frame of mind. Any day my promotion to full corporal would be published on 'Orders'. This was common knowledge among my mates, and it provoked a certain amount of 'ribbing' from Bob.

The afternoon was a happy one, with most people taking time off from the business of war. As we sat over our second cup of coffee, Bob kept up the cheerful patter.

'Don't know wevver I shall be able to come art wiv 'im, much longer,' he said, nodding in my direction.

'Why's that, then?' asked Anne, in alarm, thinking that there was some move afoot.

''E gets anuvver stripe, next week,' he grinned. 'Bleedin' corporal. Afore you know where you are, 'e'll be a sergeant, or somefing. Oo wants ter go abart wiv a sergeant!' He smirked at me. 'Alright, then, corporal – what shall we call yer – "Corporal George"?'

I looked a bit sheepish, and knew it. I still found it embarrassing, being spot-lighted like this in front of girls. I hoped Lil and Anne knew Bob was joking.

'Corporal George, eh! That sounds good, that does,' said Lil, as she drained her cup.

We all finished and prepared to make a move. Lil insisted on paying. I was ready to protest, but wink from Bob kept me quiet. The women were alright for cash, and happy to pay. Automatically, I partnered Lil as we left, as I fully realised that I was there to give Bob a clear field with Anne. We strolled around to the recreation ground, to see the last of the festivities and let our tea settle. We talked about the war, which was not one of our usual topics, in female company. As we walked along, Lil explained to me how she and Anne had left London after being bombed out, and how they had taken jobs in a factory. The work was classed as 'essential to the war effort', and so they had soon been housed in a maisonette. I found Lil easy to talk to – easier than a girl would have been; there was no need to put on an act to impress! I told her a bit about my two years in the Army and the job I would go back to after the war.

'What about yer girl, then? You've got one at 'ome, and one away, I shouldn't wonder.' she said, archly.

'No, not me,' I protested, with a laugh. 'There was a couple, in towns where I've bin stationed, but there's not one at 'ome. I've bin out with a few, though,' I boasted, not wanting to appear too green, even to Lil.

'I see – luv 'em an' leave 'em type, you are,' Lil replied.

'I don't think I've caused 'em any trouble,' I replied, airily.

It was a cool evening, but it was warming up in one respect. As we went into the lounge of *The Black Prince*, Anne said, 'We'd better get settled in for a drink, before it gets too crowded.'

We found a snug corner and settled in around a small table.

'Get 'em in, Bob,' said Lil, slipping him a pound note.

'Right-e o,' said Bob, and went up to the counter. He came back with a tray, a gin for Lil, a port and lemon, and two pints. Having distributed the drinks and given Lil her change, he went back with the tray.

'We're going to The Palais, later, Mum, if that's OK,' said Anne.

'Sure, Luv. I'll stay on here for a while,' said her mother amiably.

'What about you, George?' asked Bob.

'No – no thanks, mate,' I said, hastily. 'You carry on, an' I'll get a lift back. "Ow you going ter get back, then?' I added, as an afterthought.

'Well, there's no panic on,' said Bob – 'It's a day off, termorrer, and nobody's goin' ter miss me, first fing. An' our sergeant ain't going ter worry what time I get in, s'long as I don't make a rackit.

It was true. The battalion was spread all over the town, and there was no guard room to pass through, like in the earlier days.

'I shall 'ave ter get back,' I said. 'I've got a couple of lads ter see in the morning.' I gathered the glasses and went up to the bar.

'Two pints; a gin; and a port and lemon, please,' I ordered when I caught the harassed barmaid's eye. As I drew a ten shilling note and some change out of my pocket, I felt a hand on my arm.

'Not today, soldier.' I looked round to see a middle aged man, with an open, florid, face. 'Let me have the pleasure, son, an' Good Luck, to you and your mates.'

'Oh,' I said, in some minor confusion. 'It's very nice of you.'

'Goo on, me lad; get it down yer,' said another, grizzled looking man, drinking with my benefactor; 'an' you tell your mate the next one's in, when 'e's ready.'

'Thanks – thanks, very much,' I said even more confused.

'Not at all, son, not at all. Good Luck to yer, mate,' he said again, and patted me on the shoulder. 'Alright, Elsie, 'ow much is that, me dear?'

'That's seven and eightpence, Mr Mullins,' she said.

Back at the table, I handed the glasses round.

'You better get outside that pint, mate,' I said, to Bob. 'Bloke at the bar 'as got the next one in.'

'Strewth!' said Bob, taking a desperate swallow. He looked across to the bar. The two men gave him the 'thumbs up', and he waved his gratitude.

The place was packed. The celebrations had brought folks out, and many were making a night of it, and so the composition of the crowd was a bit different firom the usual noisy squaddies 'bulling' round the pubs.

After the third drink, Bob and Anne left.

'I expect we'll be late, Mum,' said Anne.

'Alright, duck,' said Lil.

They went, and I was left sitting there with Anne's mum, wondering how to bring proceedings to a tidy close.

'What about you, Corporal George?' asked Lil. 'I'm in no rush to go home, if you would like to stay for another.'

Another drink had appeared on the table, I didn't know quite where from. Why not! There was a friendly crowd here, and I had nothing special in mind. It would be no fun trying to find a girl on her own now that Bob was gone. Anyway, Lil was a jolly sort, and she really seemed to enjoy my company. I wouldn't have to wonder if I could find it in town tonight. To hell with the girls and what they had hidden away! I'd enjoy the evening in good company, and find my way home when the pubs shut.

'Sure Lil. Excuse me – got to make a call – be back in a mo',' I mumbled, and weaved my way out. I leant my hot forehead on the glazed tiles of the urinal as I relieved myself.

I dabbed my face with cold water, and made my way back, only to be confronted by a fresh pint. So what! I'd walk it off before I got back.

OK, Corporal George?' asked Lil, giving me an appraising glance from the other side of the table.

'Yes, I'm fine, thank you,' I said, carefully.

'Alright, soljer boy?' asked a cheerful type with a party at the next table. 'Have one with us.'

'I got one in, thanks very much,' I said, gazing bemused at the array of glasses all round.

'Right-o, mate; give the word, when you want it filling up,' came the cheerful offer.

'Good job the boxing's over,' I said, to Lil, wondering how to keep the conversation alive. 'I'd be no bloody good like this.'

'Oh, yes. Bob said you were a terror in the ring. Must say I was surprised, when I saw yer,' she said. 'You seem too quiet fer that sort of thing, and, well, not the type, really.'

'I dunno what sort I am,' I slurred. 'Yeah, I suppose it does sound daft, but I know what ter do, in the ring, when it's me an' the other bloke.'

'You'll get by,' she said. 'You come out o' this lot, an' get back 'ome, an' some nice girl'll get 'er 'ooks inter you.'

I felt myself grinning stupidly.

'Come on,' she said, after a while. 'You can see me 'ome, an' we can have another one, on the way.'

'OK, shan't be a minute,' I replied, and retired once again to the gents.

It had got dark outside, and it was a lot cooler. Lil took my arm as we walked along through the High Street, to the edge of the town. We passed the point where the 15 cwt had dropped me and Bob that afternoon, and then we turned left. Fortunately, the route was not too difficult for me to retrace – anyway, I'd only got to find the bloody sea, and turn left! I knew it wasn't really that easy, as parts of the coast were closed and occupied by the Artillery Coastal Battery boys.

'How do yer feel, Corporal George?' asked Lil.

'I feel fine,' I said. The air had cleared my head, and the beer that I had drunk was wearing off.

'Here we are,' she said. 'We live upstairs. The couple below have gone away for the weekend, to their daughter's.'

'OK then, Lil,' I said when we reached the door. 'It's been a smashing day, an' I've enjoyed it very much.'

I turned to go.

'You've got plenty of time, Corporal George, an' it'll be hours before the others get 'ome,' she said. 'You'd better 'ave a strong coffee, ter clear yer head.'

I laughed. 'Thanks, Lil, but my head's fine, after that walk, but I'll come in fer a few minutes; there's no great rush ter get back.' I hoped I was making sense – I certainly had a few more than I had meant to, and I was concentrating so as not to slur my words.

She said nothing, but quietly opened the front door, and I followed her.

'Close the door, Duck,' she said, and started up the stairs to the upper apartment. I pushed the front door, and the yale lock clicked shut. I followed her up the stairs.

Lil had disappeared. I heard the water flush, and she re-appeared.

The black-out curtains were drawn, and she pressed the light switch, bathing the room with a soft, wall light.

I went to the lavatory. I felt reasonably in control, although my head was still a bit 'woozy'.

Suddenly, I knew! Even though I was still slightly befuddled, I knew. I began to feel a bit like the green idiot that I was. The bits of the evening were falling into place, and I began to have the first inkling of the picture that was emerging.

'Had I got a girlfriend'? 'What did I do?' etc. Here was a right situation. Lil wasn't a girl, and I had thought of her only as Anne's Mum. I suddenly realised that Lil wasn't an old woman either.

'Christ,' I thought,' I must be bloody drunk!' It then occurred to me that, sturdy and older as she was, she was nevertheless a handsome woman, and must be thought desirable by most men.

She had gone through to an inner room, and I heard her sigh as she plonked her shoes down – first one, and then the other.

'Ah, that's better,' she said. She came to the communicating door, and, I noticed, without her stockings.

'Come on,' she said, quietly but confidently, and led me into the bedroom.

I felt a sense of calm, and almost relief. This time there was to be no way out, and no uncertainty.

She stretched out on the bed with a sigh, perfectly relaxed and sure. I guessed it had been a long time since she had been on a bed with a man.

'You'll 'ave ter take yer shoes off, Dearie,' she said, gently.

I felt no tension – no qualms, as I unlaced my shoes. I took off my tunic, exposing Army braces. She looked up at me, silently waiting. I wondered if she realised how bloody green I was. Anyway, there was no way back now. Lil was going to be my first, and very soon at that!

I leant across her as she lay there, and kissed her. Taking my head between her hands, she drew me down and gave me a searching, open-mouthed kiss, that left me in no doubt. I sat up. She calmly drew her dress up, baring her thighs. She had no false modesty. I gazed in wonder at the flimsy, frilly undergarment. I hadn't thought of older women wearing things like that.

'Those trousers of yours are going ter be a bit rough, Dearie,' she said, matter of fact.

As in a dream, I slipped my braces and climbed out of my trousers. She sighed softly.

'Mind me frenchies,' she said, and, taking my hand, guided me to the buttons. Trancelike, I undid them and lifted up the flap. She lay, relaxed and parted, without any fuss, as I bent over her and kissed her again. Her hands caressed my back under my shirt. I had a moment of indecision, but I needn't have worried. Her two hands moved inexorably round, guiding gently. I felt the moist, soft delight of entry. She held me while I thrust, parting wider as I pressed harder.

She clung to me a while, and kissed me, tenderly and without passion.

'Corporal George,' she said, quietly, after a while, 'you've probably no idea what you've done – you've made me realise what I have been missing.'

As for me, I felt a changed man; a world away from the George Milton of an hour ago.

'That's my first time,' I said, humbly.

She kissed me again. 'George, my dear; I find that hard to believe – I really do.' She got up and retreated to the bathroom, after kissing me again and tweaking my ear. I thought she had a softer, dreamy look. The drink had slowed me up, ironically making me a satisfying lover – more so than I knew how to be.

I prepared to leave. It had been a milestone for us both. In an unspoken way, we both knew that it was a 'one off' – a wonderful watershed.

'Goodbye, Corporal George – and thank you,' she said. 'If what you say is true, then, perhaps I've helped make a man of you. It was a wonderful evening.'

I walked part way, and then got a lift. I remembered little of the journey. I felt elated. I wanted to shout and tell everybody, but I knew I should tell nobody.

Bob sensed that something had happened, when we met on Sunday afternoon. After all, a wise boy like Bob doesn't knock around with a greenhorn like me for a year, without knowing something. A less shrewd lad than he could have worked out some of the answers.

'George,' he said, when we met at dinner time, 'you look like the cat that swallowed the bloody cream.'

'I don't know what you're on about,' I protested, in a feeble attempt to put him off the scent.

'You bloody know what I mean!' He looked at me, speculatively. 'Well, if you ain't the crafty bugger, then!' he said, admiringly.

'Why, what's up?' I asked, worried a little about Bob arriving at the truth.

'What's up?' he says. 'Alright, mate, say no more,' he went on tactfully, 'but I got me suspicions about you, mate! Well, well; who'd 'ave thought it!'

I couldn't help looking a bit uneasy.

'OK, mate,' said Bob; 'I'll belt up. I tell yer, though; you're a dark 'orse, mate – a bloody dark 'orse!'

There was no talk of a return visit to Hythe. Instinctively, Bob knew it wasn't on. He was still working on Anne, although she wasn't giving much away, as yet. Bob's instincts told him that I had crossed some bridge, and that I wouldn't be quite the same again.

He was right. Although I hadn't, in the event, had to pursue and conquer, nevertheless that first experience was a milestone – a delightful milestone which had had a profound effect on my confidence. Bob could see the change, and of course he knew the cause of it. Life was full of surprises.

Chapter Twelve

On Monday, the new promotions appeared on Orders, and my promotion to full corporal was confirmed.

HQ company boasted a tailor, and I was able to get my chevrons sewn on without much bother. This gave an additional boost to my ego as I walked into the pub on Monday evening, with the extra 'weight' on my sleeve. I did not travel alone. I was escorted by a number of buddies, from the company and elsewhere, who trooped along to help me 'wet' my stripes.

The new NCOs were kept busy. There was no time left for us to be packed off on courses, and quite a few evenings were spent sharpening up on the map and compass work, so vital to those who had to fix the lines of fire for the guns. The rising tension of the impending climax of the years of training was fully appreciated by 'Command', and the troops were kept too busy to brood.

Everybody guessed that time was nigh, and there were some unfortunate occurrences, precipitated by the rising tension.

Some of the married men were under severe pressure. Life was tough enough for the wives, especially those at home with young children, and tensions proved too much in a number of cases. The greatest pressure was liable to fall on the 'expectant fathers'. Compassionate leave was granted where possible, but war was war, and the battalion was poised for the big day, which couldn't, surely, be long delayed.

A few of the men went absent without leave. These came back, and were dealt with by the Colonel. One or two, however, did not intend to return, and they deserted. They were all tracked down. In some cases their wives had made pathetic efforts to hide them, in lofts or outhouses. The civilian and military police were experienced in winkling out such men, who had to be tracked down, without fear or favour. This was a sad, often anguishing job for the men who had to do it, and who knew the frightful pressures that might have provoked desperate action. It was hard – some of the family problems could be heart-rending – but morale could fall quickly enough for many, where domestic issues were concerned, and so any flickers of weakness had to be snuffed out.

The saddest case was that of Corporal McMann, the man who had nightmares about the Germans he had slaughtered with the Vickers in 1940. He had got married since those days, and his wife had lost their first baby, still-born, and she remained very depressed. He was given some compassionate leave, but not much.

He came back, worried and tense – his problems exacerbated by continued heart-rending letters from home. One day, he disappeared. Although it was pretty obvious where he had gone, he dodged capture for a week or two, but was eventually caught, after a furious chase over a roof. He was brought back, hand-cuffed to a sergeant, to face an inevitable court-martial.

There was no saving him. He was reduced to the ranks, and given 28 days detention. He was escorted to the detention centre, at Chatham, by a sergeant and a corporal from his company.

We met again, later. By then Private McMann was a morose, uncommunicative gunner, but he was obviously going to be a corporal number one again soon. He was too trained and experienced to be lost.

His wife died, under the rubble of her house when a land mine floated down by parachute and exploded in her front garden.

There were a number of other tragic cases, where disasters at home ate into the confidence and resolve of blokes in the battalion – but others developed a hard, hate complex, which was to make some of them ruthlessly efficient in action.

In the midst of all this, came the big exercise that we felt really was going to be the 'dress rehearsal'.

A scheme was mooted, involving deployment of a large number of troops. The area for the exercise was again, Wales.

On the morning of the move, the carriers were driven on to flat railway trucks, and the wheeled vehicles travelled by road.

The battalion rattled across the country in the troop train, travelling with two battalions of rifle regiments from the division.

We de-trained at Welshpool, and made the rest of the journey across the middle of Wales in convoy. There were many other military convoys moving in every direction.

The battalion was based once again on Rhayader, and it was good to walk through the little town and re-visit the *Castle Hotel* for a change of beer. The exercises were less arduous than the previous ones, the object being to practise liaison and co-ordination of infantry with their support arms.

However, there would be one assault exercise at the end.

As the bren carriers tracked along the narrow, steep-banked lanes, moving up to their positions, we passed lines of riflemen from our own division trudging steadily along, in single files, on either side of us. They were in battle order, camouflaged, and carrying their rifles, brens and entrenching tools easily, as though they were veterans. The MMG crews recognised a company of the Dorsets on the march.

We halted, dispersed, netted the vehicles, and rested. Eventually, company 'O' group was called for, and settled in a hollow for briefing. There was to be an attack, at brigade strength, supported by artillery, as well as the support battalion – or some of it. The support regiment was to lend a hand, with fixed-line fire from the guns, and some mortar blasting. The target area was a small range of undulating hills. The mortars would saturate the hollows beyond the first ridge. The MMGs would fire on the forward slopes, as the riflemen went in. Obviously, synchronisation was, as always in these instances, absolutely vital. 'H' hour was 1430, so that things would be completed in daylight, and so cut down the risk of anyone being shot by supporting fire – although there always was some risk.

At 1415 hours, the artillery opened up, firing their shells from behind we machine gunners. The shells passed overhead – perilously close I thought, this being my first experience of shell fire. I had thought that all shells 'screamed' overhead, but the ones that hurtled over us made a noise that reminded me of an express train. It was a fearsome, impressive noise. Then while mortars 'crumped' the target area with satisfying accuracy, the guns opened up, firing to the right of the advancing riflemen, to protect their flank; and then, ahead of them, on the forward slopes, to cover their front. Of course – need it be said – we had checked and double-checked the lines of fire of the machine guns, as an error was too dreadful to contemplate; but it still gave me a feeling of foreboding, when they chattered their chorus of death. They ceased firing, on schedule, and I took the opportunity to crawl forward to the top of the slope. I could see the ant-like figures of the infantry assaulting the forward slopes, and disappearing over the distant ridge. I couldn't help thinking that those boys would have had enough by the time they had dug their forward fox-holes.

We spent another night in Rhayader, and then rumbled across Wales, in convoy. Again, there were vehicles of all sorts, travelling in all directions. It seemed to me that the whole of the Second Army had invaded the Principality.

We halted near a forestry site, and dispersed our vehicles among the trees on the edge of a plantation. It looked as though we were going to spend the night there; it could be worse – there was plenty of good, dry bedding material here.

I strolled down the lines and found Bob, who also had time on his hands. We sauntered down a track, along the edge of the trees, and came across the vehicle lines of one of the rifle battalions – or at least, a company of them. Here, too, the vehicles were dispersed around the trees, and netted. We ran into a platoon. The riflemen, who had had a more strenuous day than we had, were resting on the grass edge to the plantation. They were sweat-stained and mud-spattered, but were recognisable by their shoulder flashes, as one of the two battalions of 'Moonrakers' in the division.

We stopped and chatted. There was a group, talking about some bloody encounter they had been in in Devizes, on their last leave.

Apparently, there had been a misunderstanding with some Americans concerning the divided loyalties of some young ladies of the town after a dance one night. According to all accounts, there had been a memorable 'punch-up', eventually settled by the MPs of two nations. There seemed to have been no great animosity – just a question of proprietory rights.

We squatted down beside the men, and Bob, in an extreme burst of generosity, passed the fags round among the members of the section. A tough looking corporal strolled up with a slung sten gun.

'Alloa, there,' he hailed us. 'You boys on that there Vickers, are you, or are you on the bloody mortar?'

'Yeah, I'm in a machine gun company,' I admitted, ''an me mate's a wireless op.'

'Well, them bloody bullets weren't fer off, this morning. I'm bloody glad your bloody 'and didn't slip any further to the left, or you'd 'ave 'ad we lot up the arse, that you would.' said the corporal, with evident feeling.

'Ah,' said another; 'I were goin' ter thumb a lift, but 'e'd 'ave shot me bloody thumb off.'

'Pity 'e didn't shoot something else off, yer randy sod,' said another. 'It's bloody big enough.'

'Ah,' added a third. 'An' it shines in the dark.'

'Not mine, Alg,' said the first, phlegmatically.

'We're goin' ter need that, Chas, ter knock froo the Siegfried Line,' quipped the corporal.

I grinned at their banter, and the others chuckled. I had taken my helmet off and squatted down beside them. A lance-corporal nearby had been busy checking a bren gun. He looked up, with a grin.

'Oi, corp,' he said, to me, 'Oi reckon oive seen you, somewhere.'

The others looked mildly interested. The lance-jack took another good squint at me, and went back to wiping the bren. After a few seconds concentration, his face cleared.

'Ah, I got yer, I reckon. You was boxing young Larry – bout afore mine,' he said.

I looked up, with interest.

'Yes,' I admitted, 'I was in the team. I can't place you, though.'

'P'haps not,' laughed the lance-jack; I was the middle weight in our team, an' I was in the bout arter yourn. I 'spect you was nursing that crack on the jaw an' belt on the nose, Larry give yer.'

'You're bloody right,' I admitted ruefully.

'Were a good fight, though,' he admitted. 'You both done well, that you did. I won my bout,' he added, matter-of-fact.

The others looked more interested. Their lance-jack was, they knew, a very tough cookie – even in a company that was made up of hard men. They knew Larry was tough, too.

'Pity young Larry's not 'ere,' said the corporal with the sten gun;

140

'e's in 'B' company, coupla miles down the track.'

'We'll 'ave ter get back,' said Bob, carefully extinguishing his fag. 'Oo knows, might be off again ter night.'

'Bloody 'ope not,' said another; 'I'm fair knackered, that I be.'

'Ta ta, then, mate; see yer in Berlin,' said Bob.

'I'll tell young Larry we sin yer,' said the lance-jack. 'Pity 'e aint 'ere, 'e'd 'ave liked to 'ave met yer.'

We set off, back up the track to our own lines.

'There's some hard boys, there,' I said.

'Yeah, bloody swede bashers,' grunted Bob, with all the superiority of the town dweller. 'You're right, though, mate. I should 'ave liked to 'ave sin that scrap they was in; s'long as I wasn't too close.'

Fortunately, there was no other move that night; and, apart from the pickets to be mounted, we were able to sleep in the bracken among the trees, covered by our waterproof groundsheets.

We entrained at Welshpool. Again, there was the tricky job of driving the carriers on to the flat railway trucks, jumping them from wagon to wagon along the line. The journey back was pleasant enough. The train rumbled and rattled, across the countryside, while the troops spread themselves out, and made the most of the rest. There were a number of card schools operating. One or two squadies, in any platoon, could be relied on to produce a pack when the occasion was ripe. Some just slept. Others stood in the corridors, watching the green fields give way to villages and towns, which in turn gave way to more green fields.

The following few days were spent quietly enough. First, there was a cleaning spell, for the equipment and the weapons, followed by various inspections to see that all was once again in order. The vehicles, too, had to be washed off and serviced, and the whole battalion again made ready for anything.

The following Saturday, I went to a dance. Bob had gone to Hythe. I had lost my old feeling of awful loneliness, although I was at a loose end. I decided to go to a little dance that I had heard of. It was inland, in the Romney area, off the Ashford Road. It was rather off the beaten track – most of the lads stayed nearer the bright lights, and tended to go to the dance hall on the Leas Cliff. I wasn't sure what had inspired me to branch out in this way. I had heard of the dance more or less by accident, talking to an ack ack gunner in a pub, a few nights back. Anyway, I felt the urge to branch out – to seek pastures new, so I found myself being ferried up the road in an American jeep, bound for Ashford. The gum-chewing GI at the wheel, was an engineer who had been across to a depot for some spare parts, and was on his way back.

OK, Tommy hop aboard,' he had said, as I had reached the edge of town. He had a long, serious face, and woe-begone expression.

'Guess you boys'll soon be on your way,' he said.

'Yeah, reckon so,' I answered, guardedly.

'Me, I goota stick to Ashford for a little while, I guess. But we recovery boys'll be chasing after yous guys later,' he added.

We drove on for a few minutes.

'Gee, I get real homesick,' he suddenly burst out. 'You're all great folks over here in this little old island, but I just want ter get back ter Minneap.'

'Been here, long?' I asked.

'Came over, March, '43,' was the answer. 'You boys get this little job over, an' let me go back home.'

'What did you do, before you were in the Army,' I asked.

'Me – I was a welder – just a plain, ordinary, mind-me-own business welder,' he said, mournfully.

We sped on. The GI obligingly turned off the road for some distance, for my benefit. The area was flat. Sheep stared at me over the gates and walls as I strolled into the village. I was a bit early, and as I passed the large village hall I could see the band arriving and beinning to unload their gear. I walked up the main street. A number of side roads branched off on either side, leading to groups of houses, or a farm. At the end of the village, the way led out into open, flat land. I retraced my steps, and came to the stone cross near the centre. The street was fairly deserted, but I got curious stares from the few people there were about. Soldiers weren't quite so common as they were in the towns, unless they were local boys on leave; certainly, soldiers who carried the colourful insignia of infantry regiments from away.

Down the street, a little way from the cross, and set well back behind the village green, lay the *Royal Oak*, a neat pub with a tight little bar and saloon. I found my way in, and ordered a pint. I turned and sat at a bench beside a wooden plank table, and got a cool nod from two old boys, who looked like shepherds. I sat at ease sipping my pint. A young, farmer-looking type came in with a precocious-looking village girl, about seventeen years old. Presumably, they were going to the dance. The girl giggled while she sipped her drink, but the 'once over' she gave me across her glass, was a cool assessment. The bar filled up, mainly with farming fraternity, or young couples stopping off on their way to somewhere. Two girls came in together. They were apparently bound for the dance.

Having had two or three drinks, I got up and obligingly put my glass on the counter, with a murmur of thanks. I had learned that such little courtesies cost nothing, and they can help keep your stock high when you're a strange feller in a close village like this. I put on my blue, regimental forage cap, which I was wearing in preference to my khaki beret, and set off for the hall. The place was filling up, and, wonder of wonders, there were more girls than men.

Quickly, without any motive other than to dance, I chose a tall, good-looking girl of about my own age, and asked her to dance. She joined me readily enough for the quick-step. I was a good dancer – of the straight forward dances – and I was pleased to find an attractive partner, who was light on her feet and responsive to my guidance on the floor. At the end of the dance, I led her to a chair and confidently sat in the one alongside. I noticed again that she was an attractive girl, with smooth features and neat, 'page boy', dark brown hair. The band struck up a waltz, and we danced. I used all the skill I possessed, and guided her round the long hall, gently but firmly. She obviously enjoyed dancing. She was wearing flat heeled shoes, and she was able to slide them gracefully on the powdered floor.

'You dance nicely,' she said, at the end of the waltz.

'You're not so bad yourself,' I said, as I steered her by the arm to a seat.

'You're not from around here, are you?' she asked.

I told her that I had come out from Folkstone for a change and that I was here for the first time.

'How will you get back?' she asked.

'I'll walk,' I replied, airily.

'It's quite a long way, you know,' she warmed.

'That's OK, I'm used to it,' I laughed. 'I've done a lot of walking in this job. Anyway, it's a nice evening, and it doesn't matter if I'm a bit late.' You never know your luck, and I decided that I ought to make that point clear, just in case there were to be any interesting developments.

After another two or three dances, they announced the palais glide. I was not too keen, and I asked her if she would care to go for a drink.

'Alright,' she said, after a slight hesitation, 'it's not far, and I'll go and get my coat.'

We set out, and, instead of making for the *Royal Oak*, she led the way, through an alley, to a tiny pub near a small housing estate. It was almost empty. I settled for half a pint this time, and bought the girl a port.

'What's your name?' I asked her. 'I'm George, and, as I said, I'm from Folkstone.'

'I'm Joan,' she said, 'and I live just down the road.'

We finished our drinks and walked back, along the alley. She held my arm as we negotiated the dark footpath, bordered by a hedge. She showed no great desire to dally, and I felt under no pressure to try anything. I felt relaxed, and I was really enjoying the evening. It was a pleasant change from the 'occupied' towns on the coast; there was no doubt that the competition was less keen. I was with an attractive dancing partner who was apparently happy to stick with me. Although she nodded and spoke to a number of lads, whom she obviously, knew, she stayed with me throughout the evening. She was attractive and good company.

She was easy to talk to, during and between dances. I had to tell her something of my life as a soldier, and where I came from, and so on. The conversation remained on a friendly, if not very intimate level, and she clearly enjoyed the dancing.

Latish on in the evening, while an 'Excuse Me' dance was on, she retired to 'powder her nose'. Looking round, I saw a soldier, older than me, from the REME, talking to a few civvies. He nodded to me casually, and I strolled in his direction.

'Hi there, Corp,' said the REME man. 'What brings you round here. From Folkstone, aren't you?'

'Yeah,' I replied, easily; 'Thought I'd come out this way for a change; quite nice here, ain't it.'

'It's OK,' agreed the REME soldier. 'I live in the next village, an' I've bin lookin' in on this Saturday 'hop' for years. See you've got yerself off with our Joan, then.' He looked at me with a faint grin. 'Haven't met her before, have you?'

'No, this is the first time I've bin here,' I said.

'Taking her home, are you?' he asked, still grinning.

'Yeah, I hope so, why not?'

He looked at me, carefully.

'Quite a nice girl, is Joan. Bin round with one or two fellers, she has. Used ter go out with Fred – feller I know; but 'e's bin sent up Catterick way.'

He paused, apparently wondering how much more he could tell me. I seemed to have made a reasonable impression on him, and he seemed friendly.

'Can I give you a tip – no offence?' he said, finally.

'Sure; course you can,' I replied.

'Well, I know the district, like.' He hesitated. 'Young Joan's OK, an' you just might be lucky there, but she's got ter like yer quite a bit, if yer want ter take any liberties, like.' He went on, more surely. 'Most of the fellers have bin unlucky, an' they get put off, 'cause they can do alright somewhere else. You've done alright, tonight, I can see that, 'cause she don't often dance with the same feller, all night – an' you just might – who knows?'

Joan could be seen, coming out of the cloakroom at the far end of the hall.

'Hope you don't mind me telling yer, mate,' he said, as he moved away.

'No, mate; thanks very much,' I murmured.

'Good luck, then,' he said, and turned away quickly.

She smiled cheerfully as I swept her straight into a quickstep.

After that came one of those 'smooth,' 'smoochie' waltzes, where the lights go down and the spotlight picks out the lucky winner. I didn't want any spotlight. I had been thinking about the soldier's advice, and I decided that I should have to make the running. As the lights went down, I ventured to hold her closer, and, boldly, I kissed her on the ear. This seemed to please her, as she held on tightly. Following this initial success, I moved my head round, found her lips, and brushed them lightly. Subtley, a change had taken place in our relationship, and I had positively established my claim to take her home.

Half way through the last dance, she kissed me lightly on the nose.

'I'll fetch my coat,' she said.

It was a fine night. I guided her out, and we went down the alley which led to the little pub. I had got my arm round her waist, and she clasped my protective hand firmly. The way led along a side alley and came out at the back of some houses, each of which had a garden gate leading down to the back door.

'Here we are,' she said. 'I shall have to go soon, or my dad'll wonder where I've got to.'

'You can wait a minute,' I said, drawing her against a sloping willow tree. It was very dark there. I turned her against the sloping trunk, and trapped her with my arms. I kissed her, gently, searchingly. She clung to me for a moment.

'I must go in,' she said, again.

'Just a little while longer,' I begged, and kissed her again, a good deal harder. She seemed a little restless, and made as though to escape from the prison of my arms. But I kept them there, and she stayed.

Gently, and very cautiously, I explored her blouse, undoing the three buttons, and freeing her breast from its 'cage'.

'Don't,' she begged, becoming more agitated as I caressed and kissed. 'You mustn't – I'll be late,' She was pleading rather than forbidding, I thought.

'Don't worry, Joan,' I said, more urgently and positively now that I had got so far, 'I'll be careful.'

Moving my hands, slowly but surely, and with no hesitation, I held her close, and ran my right hand up between her thighs. She gasped, with desperation or agitation, when I contacted the smooth flesh, above her stockings. I held her, very firmly, with an encircling left arm, while my right hand roved, probed and explored.

'No; I shall have to go; you mustn't do anything more.' she gasped, beseechingly.

'Alright; don't worry,' I said, calmly; 'I'm going to be careful; you don't have to worry.' I was trying hard to overcome her qualms as I pressed closer to her, caging her protectively against the tree.

'Oh, you mustn't do anything else. It's getting late. They'll wonder where I am!' she gasped as I investigated the intricacies of her underwear. I couldn't help thinking, even then, that she seemed more worried about the time than what I was going to do to her.

'Come on,' I said, gently, now, but with a degree of firmness; 'You'll be OK.'

She caught her breath, desperately almost, as I closed on her, drawing up the front of her skirt and petticoat. She seemed to become more agitated as, almost mercilessly now, I found a way past her underclothes and, adjusting my position, pressed home, leaning her back against the sloping trunk.

At some indeterminate point, when I had drawn aside the obstructing garment, she had 'conceded', and held me, with both arms, making small moaning noises, as she waited for her moment of 'release'.

It came just before I withdrew, as I had promised. She gasped, and I had a pang of guilt. There was no need. To my amazement and puzzlement, her whole manner had changed. She held on to me for a moment, and kissed me, tenderly and firmly.

'You'll have to go,' she said. Now that the moon was casting a little light, I could see that she was smiling.

'It has been a marvellous evening,' she said.

There was no talk of meeting again. She had given in to me, eventually, without regret, and we had shared a memorable, albeit, brief relationship. I was almost overwhelmed with delight and success, and I knew that she was pleased that I had overcome her initial resistance, and left her feeling so 'at peace'. She knew I would go, now. We had 'made' it, and I sensed that she was content to leave it at that.

I set off at a smart pace, through the village and along the narrow lane, to the main Ashford Road. I turned right, and moved off, at a brisk trot. I had covered about two miles, when I heard the sound of a motor bike coming up behind me, its masked headlight giving a very faint glow on the road ahead. The moon was bright, and I was silhouetted as the rider approached. As he drew near, I noticed that he was an Army rider.

'I thought so,' said the rider. 'I sin you, ararnd Shornecliffe, mate. What the bloody 'ell are you doin' out 'ere this time o' night?' The DRs red and yellow flashes could be seen on his sleeve. He was wearing a sleeveless leather coat, and his regimental colours could also be seen on his helmet.

'Christ! What are you doing here, this time of night, yourself, then?' I replied, very pleased to see him.

'Never you mind what I bin on – had a message ter take ter Div. HQ – important, so they say. I'm in HQ company. Come on, then; get on the bloody seat, or we'll be 'ere all bleedin' night.'

The DR kicked his machine into life, while I, thankfully, straddled the pillion.

'Bin wavin' it at the poor little girls, again, I bet,' said the driver, laconically.

'To bloody true,' I admitted. 'It took a bloody long time ter get 'er ter let me 'ave it, but I got there!'

'Lucky sod,' said the other, without malice. 'Some blokes 'ave all the bloody luck. Only ride I get is on this bleedin' bike.'

He pulled the goggles over his eyes, toed the bike into gear, and away we went. I could hardly believe my luck. I 'rode' the bends on the road smoothly, and in a very short time, we came to the outskirts of Folkstone. Here, the DR pulled up, and I quickly got off. Thanking my benefactor, I made my way back to the convent. I now had a little 'cell' of my own, so I caused no disturbance as I eased myself between the blankets, and feel fast asleep.

Sunday morning was easy. There were no duties and no parades. I couldn't help wondering what Bob was going to say, when I told him my story – and tell him, I certainly would!

I saw him in the dinner queue, and we arranged to meet in the evening.

'Have I got something to tell you, mate!' was all I would tell him. I wrote a letter, and went in to tea. After tea, I made my bed down and strolled into town. It was a fine day. Summer was taking over from the late spring, and the beach below the cliffs looked clean and inviting – very different from the cold, snow covered shore of last winter.

I called in at Bob's billet, where my mate was putting the final polish to his shoes.

'Allo, mate,' he quipped, when he saw me. 'Shan't be a mo'. Just puttin' a gimp on me old shoes. Where's me titfer, then?'

He hopped around, getting ready to come out. I sat on a bunk, and exchanged a few words with the wireless and line boys, who occupied most of the billet. I knew most of them. Geoff Collard was there. He had ended up as a 22 set operator in a bren carrier, and he seemed to have settled happily. He wasn't one for a booze up, or chasing the skirt, but he was a generous, good-hearted lad, and he had become popular with the others. He had taken a lot of leg-pulling in his time, but he had weathered it well.

At last, Bob was all set. He had made his bed down, and left everything as he wanted it. We set out to do the rounds. A quiet drink was on the programme – no women or singing.

'How was Anne, then?' I asked, remembering that Bob had been over to see her the day before. I was bursting to let him in on my news, but I made it wait.

'I dunno what ter make of it, mate,' said Bob, uneasily. 'Right's right, cocker. I dunno what to do abart it. I don't mind a bit of 'ow's yer farver, but, well, she's a good kid, an' I don't fink I can do it to 'er. D'yer know, I don't fink she's 'ad it – straight up – s'fact. I'm bloody sure she ain't. She's gettin' a bit serious, an' she's eager. Fing is, she's set 'er 'at at me.'

Poor old Bob. He had to burn his fingers, it was on the cards.

'Yer luck's in, then, mate,' was all I would say.

'Come off it, George,' he said, looking almost ashamed of his scruples.

'Ding, dong, ding dong,,' I chimed, unable to resist the temptation.

'OK, OK, I got the message. Anyway, I got enough troubles o' that sort.' He looked uncomfortable. 'Besides, we ain't goin' ter be 'ere, much longer.'

'Well, we all know that, don't we?' I answered, shortly.

'Yeah; OK, OK. But there's messages comin' froo. The area's goin' ter fill up, mate. There's a lot o' stuff on the move, an' it ain't games, this time, I reckon.' Bob paused. 'Just don't say nuffin', mate. You know me, can't keep me bloody marf shut!'

'Thanks, mate,' I said, sombrely. 'I know that ain't true. Anyway, it's not really news, is it.' I paused. 'How was Lil, by the way,' I added, casually.

Bob gave me a wise, know-all look.

'She's OK, George.' He paused, and looked hard at me. I tried to maintain a cool look back, but I felt myself going a bit red.

'You're a crafty one, mate. 'Oo'd 'ave thought it.' He sighed. 'Tell us, though mate,' he said suddenly, almost catching me off guard, 'was she nice?'

I didn't reply.

'Alright,' he conceded, 'but she asked after yer, George. She had a look in 'er eye that could only mean one thing.'

'What do you mean,' I dared.

'She's 'ad it, mate. First time fer a long time. I could tell.' He paused. 'If it wasn't you, I can't imagine 'oo else it could be.'

'Let me tell yer about yesterday,' I said, quickly, anxious to get off the subject. 'You're goin' ter find this 'ard ter credit, mate.'

'Come on, then; tell yer Uncle Bob,' he said, brightly.

I told him. I described the village, the journey, and the dance. I couldn't help enthusing over the star qualities of Joan; the tip that the REME man had given me, and the exciting hour by the back gate.

He interrupted once or twice with a question or an exclamation. When I told him about her pleadings and protests, ending in willing submission, I expected not to be believed.

'Well I never did!' exclaimed Bob. 'Funny fings, women. "Stop it I like it" touch.' He adopted an air of shocked concern. 'Bloody, 'ell mate; there's no 'olding you. Seems I shall 'ave ter tag along fer a few tips.' He looked at me, with something akin to awe.

Things were building up. For so long we had seen troops from just our own circle – platoon, company, battalion, and, of course, there had been divisional maneouvres. Now, the area was filling up. There could no longer be any escaping the evidence – it was all going to happen, here, in the South – but where?

The order came through on Monday. From now on, kit was to be packed and ready. There would be no passes of any sort. There would be a curfew.

On Tuesday, I went with a driver, in a 15cwt truck, inland to a depot for some urgent spares. It was a nice day for a run out, and it all made a pleasant change. The roads were surprisingly clear of traffic – even military traffic was pretty scarce.

We collected our parts, but it had all taken us a bit longer than we had expected. On the way back, we were surprisingly directed to a side road by a motor-cycle MP. We were trapped there for two hours, but we were able to witness the sight of our lives. The road became filled with steadily moving convoys – and what convoys. Escorted by swarms of DRs, they poured south in endless streams – all moving in, without hitch or hold-up. They rolled by in their hundreds; trucks, carriers, light armour. There were TCVs, full of men. The men were quiet. There wasn't the usual singing and cat-calling, that one associated with truck loads of squadies. Anyway, there was nobody to cat-call to.

As the stream continued, we both stood and stared, feeling so choked with emotion that we both found it almost too much to speak. What was there to say? I know that, as I stood there, there were tears on my cheek, and I didn't care who saw them, as I watched the columns roll by. There were units I hadn't seen before. I picked out a battalion of 'Monmouths'. There were battalions of northern regiments; there were Signals, RECCE, light artillery, more light armour – and, yes, some infantry support, with their carriers rumbling along. All the troops were in battle order, camouflaged, and, seemingly, ready for anything. On and on they came. It was no exercise. They were here to stay. The southern coast was filling up. Where would they all be billeted? Surely, this could not be kept a secret.

We looked at each other; we grabbed each other's arms.

'Strewth: my bloody oath!' said my driver.

My eyes were still moist, and I didn't care. I still felt 'choked': we both did.

'Look at 'em' I said with elation. 'All on our bloody side, too! Who's going ter stop that lot?'

'We're goin' ter 'ave a bit of 'elp, an' that's fer sure,' said the other. 'Blind ol' Riley – just look at that lot!' he went on, as a stream of carriers, carrying RNFs, went rattling by.

After two hours, things quietened down. A burly police corporal, sten gun slung, and a scrim net square knotted around his neck, drew up on his 'Matchless', and called me over to where he straddled his bike.

'Nearly got caught up in the bloody war, you did,' he said, with a hard grin. 'You can get on, now. Don't hang about, though, 'cause there's a lot more, coming down.'

He glanced behind, gave a wave of his left hand, and pulled away after the tail of the convoy.

We drove back, our minds in a whirl – too full to say very much.

Things were happening, back in our area, as well.

All ranks were confined to billet areas. Then came the order to pack the last bits and pieces. Full marching order was prepared, and spare kit was tied in kit bags, to travel separately by truck.

During the night, the battalion transport formed up along the coast road, duly fuelled. There was a sense of urgency. The battalion was formed up to move. As each platoon and company moved into line, the convoy grew. Ammunition had been issued for personal weapons during the night, and I had stashed two sten magazines in my pouches.

There were no goodbyes. By morning, we were gone – the convoy rumbling through the night, the vehicles rolling along with masked lights.

The town woke up to see the rear party of home-based troops clearing up, leaving little trace of the occupation of weeks. There were, of course, the memories: the noisy soldiers in the pubs; the details marching down the streets at meal times; the crowded dance halls; the columns of carriers and trucks; the cheerful backchat of the London boys in the streets and shops. For the girls, the time had come that they knew would come. The town would be quiet, less crowded, and infinitely more dull.

By dawn, the battalion had arrived at some camp in Sussex. It was a camp that had recently been vacated by another unit. On the way, someone had recognised Crowborough. No one was going anywhere. It was a hutted camp, and there was a NAAFI – and that was about it. A meal had been prepared, by a resident catering staff. 'Irons' were dug out from small packs; everything else was left, packed up. Vehicles were deployed among the trees at the southern edge of the camp.

Bob came down to 'A' company lines, from HQ company. He was still Bob – cheerful, uncrushable Bob, with, perhaps, a little less banter than usual.

'Whatcher, mates,' he hailed, as he came into our hut; 'anybody ready fer a night dahn tahn, then?'

A couple of the lads scowled at him. Unperturbed, he carried on; ''Cept there ain't any bloody tahn, an', even if there was, there's guards all around the bleedin' camp – an' they ain't our fellers eiver.'

There were knowing glances among the members of the platoon. This was nasty. This was no exercise – not this time. This wasn't the Army buggering us about again, surely.

'Reckon them NAAFI girls are goin' ter be busy, ternight,' said one.

We were paraded, inspected, and our weapons checked. The MT staff did the daily tasks on their vehicles. NCOs checked the ammunition, carried by the men and with the guns.

Next morning, there was PT – early, just to keep us on our toes.

It was after breakfast that the troops were paraded, by companies, and we were told the momentous – the stupendous – news. Major Smythe addressed 'A' company, in the mess hut.

'Some of our comrades have landed this morning on the beaches of Northern France,' he said. 'The Americans have large forces further west.'

The silence was electric.

Major Smythe hesitated, then continued. 'This is not a raid, men. We're going there to stay.'

'We!' muttered someone, by my right ear. 'Muck our luck, then!'

'There isn't much more I can tell you,' went on the company commander. 'It's what we've trained so hard for – all of us. It's no news to you to know that we shall be there soon enough.'
He paused again.

'You're a fine company,' he said, hesitantly, 'and I know you will give a good account of yourselves. I don't want to say much about the regiment of which you are a part. It has a reputation and a tradition.'

He picked up his cap from the table in front of him, and made to leave.

'Oh, yes. If anyone has any personal problems that I might be able to help with, please arrange to see me through your platoon commander.'

This time, he had finished.

'Thank you, sarn't major,' he snapped.

As he trooped out with the other officers, the CSM jerked us all to our feet, and to attention.

'Thank you, sir.' he barked, and saluted.

The platoons were then reseated, while the CSM had a few words.

'You know the drill,' he commenced. 'You can't go out, so don't try. No mail will be posted till further notice. Be ready to move, at any time. I'd like ter see the sergeants, fer a few minutes. The rest of you can fall out.'

We fell out. Nobody said very much. After all this waiting and preparing, it seemed in a funny way a bit of an anti-climax.

I sat on my bunk. I felt easy, relaxed. So. Well, I'd joined this outfit – it had been all my idea. Certainly, we had been well-trained – as well as anybody, I'd say.

I sat, with my feet on the floor, hands between my knees, and I let my mind wander back over the last two years. I thought of the PTW, where it had all began, 'firing' wooden rounds from an old rifle, while Sergeant Jacks went from man to man, scowling fiercely. Good old Jacks! I wondered how many rookies he had dealt with since then. Come to think of it, Corporal Foot still owed me a shilling for chucking that grenade. I remembered the run when John Lewin and I had gone ahead. Then there was that mile, on sports day; and that ten days in dock, with that nice, cool nursing sister. Other shadows flitted past. Dear old Bill Smith, Paddy Logan, Jim Dodson, Corporal Brown. There was Chester, and *The Jolly Boatmen,* and that trooper, lying on the grass with that girl. Girls! They flashed across my mind's eye, and I began to feel a bit choked. Dear Stella – she had been my first real heartache. How was she? I hoped her marriage had worked out. And what about Joyce? Had she surrendered her 'all', after a dance one night, to some lucky trainee? And Heather. I'd walked all the bloody way to Hanwell for her, and I hadn't even seen the colour of her knickers! I should have given her a 'thumping' on the settee, and then let her bloody civvy get on with it. Bill Turley had had the right idea – 'Come across with it, girl, or I'll go somewhere else.' Bill was still with us, in the mortar company.

Hounslow had been bloody regimental. I wasn't too sorry to leave there. That bloody route march! I remembered silly things – like the dead fish in the river, blasted by the bakelite grenade – the sultry looking girl in *The Red Lion,* with that smooth civvy: God! She would have made a lovely grind!

I remembered the boxing. I hoped those rifle regiment boys got through this lot, OK. Some weren't going to make it. I looked around the hut, at the members of the platoon, smoking, arguing, swearing, sitting about. I couldn't help wondering which of them would go under. I thought of my old school, and that list of names they read out every 11 November. Would my name be on the next list, I wondered, to be read out to a lot of bored grammar school kids in the future?

Good old Lil! She had been lovely. What a girl! I thought back over that memorable hour in the maisonette, when she had done it all, for me. I remembered the softness of her, and the gentle way she had shown me 'how'. What a bloody waste it would be if she didn't get a bloke to keep her busy. Joan – Oh, what a little struggle by the willow tree that had been. She was a nice girl, in every way, even if she had, finally, held her skirt up while I did it. Funny, too, how happy she was after all that fuss. I wondered what life had in store for her.

I wondered what the lads were doing at work. I expect it was the same routine, trying to make paint from new materials, as the recognised ingredients became unavailable. Who was that simpering little bitch in the office? Pauline, that was her name. I couldn't help thinking what I could do to her, if she was on the bunk with me right now. Ah well, I'd give her a bloody fright when I got out of this lot. I knew a lot more about her sort now. I smiled to myself. I reckoned I'd have a good try to stretch her out in the park next summer, when we had done this job. I wondered whether she had button-up ones. No chance. I'd probably find a tight-fitting, brief pair, that would have to be dragged off.

'NAAFI's open, Corp.'

'Right-o, Pete.' I stirred, and stood up. 'I'll be along, in a minute – could do with a wad.'

Bob was there, at the counter. Bob – how typical he was of many of the boys from the back streets of the capital – cheerful, uncrushable, tough, and desperately loyal to a mate. I owed a lot to Bob.

'Whatcher, Cock! You're just in bleedin' time ter buy the tea an' wads,' was his greeting.

'Cheeky sod,' I said, without malice, making for the counter. I ordered the tea and wads. The NAAFI girl gave me a smile.

'Hello, Rose,' I said. 'What's it like, then, to be trapped in camp with all these randy men then? You lucky girl.'

She smiled as she handed me my change. She was just a young Sussex girl, but she knew pretty well what was on. This was history in the making. Sometimes, she wanted to cry when she saw them, laughing and joking, so fit and active.

I couldn't keep quiet. 'When's my turn for a little wriggle, then?' I said with a grin, pulling her forward for a kiss.

'You can go to the top of the queue, you know that,' she said, very sombrely.

I shut up. I knew she was a nice girl, and I knew she was emotionally charged by the awe of the situation – weren't we all! I could quite likely play on the heroics and get her to come across, after a bit of persuasion.

'You hang on to it, Rose,' I said, gruffly, 'until some lucky squadie in the Sussex comes back and takes you into the woods. But when he does – give him a treat – I expect the poor bugger will have earned it.'

Bob was quieter than usual. I didn't press. I was pretty sure I knew his trouble, and there was little I could do to help. I knew he was worried about his girl in hospital. She was coming along, OK, but he was wondering what would happen to her if he didn't come back. Also, there was his old Mum. He was their only son, born late, when they had almost given up hope. Old Bob – still worrying about others, when he was going to have enough on his plate.

We stayed there for two more days. On the third evening, the vehicles lined up, and we left – without any fuss.

The locals heard the trucks and carriers rumbling through the night. It happened, nearly every night.

'Bloody docks, this time,' said my No 2 gunner.

We drew in, through the gates of a pre-war barracks. Another unit had just pulled out.

Several days passed.

About two weeks after D-Day, we got another summons to move. This time, it WAS the docks.

We drove the vehicles down, a few at a time. There were the transports, just as they had been in training, when we had gone out at nights and shinned up and down the assault netting, and we had lost a good officer, who had fallen and broken his back. Along one side of the craft, scaling nets were just visible.

It was a fine night. The soldiers were shown their alloted deck space, and the drivers went away to help check the lashing to the vehicles, so they wouldn't move at sea.

There was movement. The transport crept away, down the estuary, to join the others that could be seen through the gloom. The moon cast a band of light across the water.

The flotilla set out for the Channel.

The waiting was over.

Errata

p.	47	line 2 of final paragraph: 1866 to read 1862

p.   47   line 2 of final paragraph: 1866 to read 1862
          line 3: delete parenthesis
p.   63   line 3 of final paragraph to begin
          'Monmouthshire by Henry Willis and Sons
          of London'
p. 106   lines 9 and 10: delete 'as a minor soloist
          in more than one performance of Aida'
p. 134   line 11: 1976 to read 1975
p. 141   line 5: 'complimented' to read 'complemented'
p. 147   under BEETHOVEN, Mass in C, '1978' to read
          '1979'
p. 148   line 17 under BLISS, '1963' to read '1966'
p. 159   column 2, line 2: to read 'M. Rawnsley
          1977- (joint)'
p. 160   under heading 'Executive Committee':
          'R.A. Barraclough' to read 'R. Barraclough'
          and 'Mrs. M. Walker' to read 'Mrs. M.W. Walker'
p. 161   column 2, line 4: to read 'Mrs. J. Mair'
                    line 35: to read 'Mrs. S. Beatty'
p. 162   all names listed in column 3 under the
          heading 'First Basses' should appear under
          the heading 'Second Basses'
p. 174   column 1, line 27 'Haywood, D.G.A.' to read
          'Haywood, G.D.A.' column 2, line 40 to read '2'
p. 179   column 2, line 10: omit '106' under reference